# THE PASTORAL HERITAGE
# OF BRITAIN

SNOW IN YORKSHIRE

Bringing down sheep from the Fells above the little Dales village of Thorpe, near Grassington.

# THE
# PASTORAL HERITAGE
# OF BRITAIN

*A Geographical Study*

BY

## E. H. CARRIER
M.A., M.Sc., F.R.Hist.S.

LONDON
## CHRISTOPHERS
22 BERNERS STREET, W.1

MELBOURNE: SYDNEY: WELLINGTON: CAPE TOWN: TORONTO

*First Published in 1936*

Made and Printed in Great Britain by Butler & Tanner Ltd., Frome and London

*Be thou diligent to know the state of thy flocks, and look well to thy herds.*

PROVERBS xxvii. 23.

# PREFACE

THIS book is not a treatise on practical agriculture, but an environmental study. Formal geography, tables of statistics and details of manufacturing processes have been excluded, it being assumed that my readers are already acquainted with the general climatic, topographical and geological factors of Britain, while manufacturing processes can be better studied elsewhere. The emphasis has been placed upon the pastoral utilization of our grasslands and heaths, our ploughed fields and farmyards, life from the point of view of the cattle and sheep, the historical and social episodes that have arisen out of the pastoral industry, and like matters. The vastness of the subject has made selection of material necessary, and in the following pages the theme has been developed almost entirely upon the lines of sheep and cattle and the pastoral farming whereby their food is secured.

At the moment, the pastoral industry is undergoing a partial eclipse, and certain procedures of long standing have quite recently disappeared over large areas, but their ancient establishment and possibility of their return may perhaps justify their place in this narration, as well as their persistence in some of the more remote districts.

I should like to take this opportunity of thanking Dr. E. W. Russell (Rothamsted Experimental Station,

Harpenden) for his very valuable help and criticism, and also the Reverend R. Logan Mitchell, of Lerwick, Shetland, and Miss Phyllis Cowell, M.A., for kindly reading my proofs. Thanks are likewise due to the Reverend R. Logan Mitchell for the information he has collected for me, and to the United Dairies, Ltd., and the Milk Marketing Board, for similar assistance.

E. H. CARRIER

# CONTENTS

CONTENTS

## PART III

### THE LEGACY

# ILLUSTRATIONS, MAPS AND DIAGRAMS

# BRIEF NOMENCLATURE

## SHEEP

i. When first born, lambs (ewe or female, ram or male) in general till 12 or 14 months old. ii. Weaning to first shearing (about $1\frac{1}{4}$ years) hogs, hoggs, hoggets, tegs (tags, on account of the tapering of the unshorn locks). iii. After first shearing the male lamb is a shearling. iv. After July 1st ewe-lambs born the previous year are ewes, and castrated ram-lambs are wethers. v. Adult uncastrated male sheep are tups. vi. After first shearing female lambs are called gimmers, two-toothed, etc., according to locality ; female lambs and ewes making part of the breeding stock are two shear, three shear, four toothed, six toothed and full mouthed, according to age. vii. Breeding ewes are called stock ewes. viii. An old ewe of worn teeth is a crone. ix. Store sheep are growing or young sheep neither belonging to the breeding stock nor being fattened. x. A couple is a ewe and its lamb.

## CATTLE

i. When first born, calves. ii. A female calf is a heifer from calf period to first or second calving, according to locality ; a male calf is a bull calf. iii. Steers are castrated males. iv. From four years old a steer is known as an ox. v. Bullocks, a loose term often used for steers and oxen. vi. Bull, the adult, uncastrated male. vii. Store cattle are growing or young cattle neither belonging to the breeding stock, dairy herd, nor being fattened.

# PART I
## THE PRESENT

## CHAPTER I

# THE FEEDING GROUNDS

THE different herbages and root crops which form the main and sometimes the only food of sheep and cattle make the subject of this chapter. They include the natural grassland or permanent pastures, the temporary pastures or leys, and arable fields wherein green and root crops are grown for the use of the farm livestock. To achieve their full excellence these pastures require the adequate rainfall throughout the year and relatively mild temperatures of the temperate zone, and to the Atlantic influences we owe that plenitude of rain which assists so largely in weathering and watering the soil that our natural pastures in general furnish a reliable source of food without much expenditure of care or money. Great Britain is so naturally a pastoral country that our agriculture is largely and might be even further stimulated by this fact.

The natural grasslands predominate under some or all of these conditions—a high rainfall with a fairly uniform distribution throughout the year, and ground inaccessible or too infertile for cultivation, though excessive infertility may result in mountain pastures of the heath or poor moorland type. The low-lying districts along river valleys where heavy soil makes cultivation costly, can give a rich and profitable grazing ; otherwise the permanent grassland is in general a feature of the upland country of the north, west, and south.

The long existence of this grassland, whose plants

4 THE PASTORAL HERITAGE OF BRITAIN [PT. I

have established themselves according to conditions of relief, climate, and quality of soil, has earned for it the name of permanent.  Given competing seeds, the richest soil produces the best pasture grasses, poorer ones becoming increasingly dominant as fertility decreases. The best pastures contain much red or white wild clover, the latter being of pre-eminent value.  True grasses such as perennial rye grass, meadow fox-tail, cocksfoot, meadow fescue, and cat's tail (or timothy) are also present in great quantities and in proportions depending upon depth of soil, conditions of climate, etc.  The rich old sod of these pastures is often several inches thick, its excellence being the result of a hundred years of growth and grazing, the soil minerals having been removed neither by mowing of the grass nor milking of herds.

A slightly less excellent pasture may contain good growths of such grasses as the rough stalked meadow grass, squirrel's tail or meadow barley grass, golden oat grass, and a fair proportion of these together with a few poorer grasses or weeds such as the bromes, Yorkshire fog, quaking grass, and common bent.  These last grasses are dominant on very poor pastures, and there will be additional weed grasses and possibly moss.

Our mountain pastures and heaths are generally known as rough grazings.  Between 1918 and 1928 much of the arable land in downland districts was allowed to " tumble down " to rough grazing.  Such land formerly grew corn, but the too successful foreign competition has destroyed this agriculture by making it unprofitable.

Sheep fescue is the dominant grass of the downland. The herbage is small but nourishing, feeding large flocks of sheep, especially in the summer.  Occasionally cattle browse these pastures.

Water is also a necessity for flocks and herds.  Running water is the best ; stagnant water, always injurious, becomes even more so when cattle customarily stand in it. On the other hand, the pastures must be well drained, or else rank grass will spring up and make a breeding ground for parasites which weaken and even kill the livestock they attack. The appearance of rushes, sedges, and tussocks gives warning that the drainage is becoming deficient.

The grazing season in general includes three periods of varying length according to locality. From April to hay time at the end of July is the period of the first and richest " bite ". The pasture, so far unsoiled by the animals, is " sweet ", and the better-grade grasses thrive richly upon the food that has accumulated in the soil since the last grazing. This young grass, not as yet very securely fixed in the ground, should be grazed only sparingly by sheep, whose close nibbling might injure it. The end of hay time to October marks a second grazing period. The soil is a little exhausted and lower-grade grasses come to the fore. Cattle using these pastures require a supplementary feed of tares, cabbages, maize, etc. The third period extends from October to winter. The " bite " is now at its poorest and the bromes, Yorkshire fog, bents, and other grasses of lower feeding value which form the major part of this growth, make it necessary to give additional rations of cattle cake. In Central England, and especially in the south-east Midlands, young cattle are taken off this pasture early in the third period ; in other parts they spend the winter out of doors, unless the weather be exceptionally severe. The winter grazing of the lightly-treading sheep does little harm to the not infrequently soft soil, and is of especial manurial benefit when pasturing takes place on the mown aftermath.

It goes without saying that good pastures should be

kept clear of weeds injurious to livestock; from the shade hedge or ditch plants cows may nibble off shoots which spoil the flavour of the milk, and some of the not unusual but obnoxious growths are meadow saffron, Jack-of-the-hedge, and various garlic plants.

The distinction between permanent grassland and meadow is a matter of controversy. The term " meadow " is often restricted to lowland grassland near flowing water, which presumably benefits the herbage both as water and on account of the mists arising from it; upland pastures are then regarded as permanent. Meadowland is sometimes defined as mown grassland, in contrast to grasslands which are never cut; sometimes the differentiation is made between grazing land and mown grasslands, an inconsistent distinction, since some meadows are alternately mown and grazed. Moreover, such grazings greatly affect the meadowland, especially if cropped by sheep, whose close nibbling prunes the upspringing grasses, thus promoting a thicker bottom growth which may be much assisted by the " treading " of the little " golden hoof ".

In certain districts grasslands are watered somewhat elaborately through man's manipulation of neighbouring streams, an irrigation process which enhances the value of the grass either for hay or for the temporary grazing of stock. Such irrigated or water meadows are found on the hill slopes of east Yorkshire, in the Dove Valley in Derbyshire, and along the Rivers Kennet, Churn, Severn, Avon, Itchen, and Test.

Irrigated grassland also occurs in the valleys of many rivers and brooks of Worcestershire and Devon. The greatest proportion of English irrigation is situated in our south and south-western counties.[1]

[1] For general methods of carrying out the irrigation see Chapter XII.

The virtue of this artificial watering lies in the fact that land is kept flooded for a longer or shorter period by a thin sheet of moving water. It takes place mainly in the winter months, when the moving water is warmer than the normal temperature of the ground. Atmospheric oxygen is entangled in it, and its dissolved mineral and organic constituents assist the enrichment of the soil.

The annual routine of these irrigated meadows varies with the climate and use to which the grass is to be put. As a rule, the ewes and lambs eat off the early spring feed (mid-March to April), grazing after the dew has gone till about 4 or 5 p.m. The day's portion is marked off by hurdles, the lambs running on ahead through small holes or creeps in the hurdles to secure the first and richest bite. This pasturage may tide the farmer over a difficult time till his early summer catch crops [1] are ready. Later, after some further watering at need, the grass is " laid up " for hay, and cut about the end of June or beginning of July. This harvest is succeeded by a renewed watering to promote autumn grazing, and when the meadow is dry, dairy cows or other stock are put upon it until the end of the autumn season. The rapid growth of the herbage due to the summer watering results in the retention of much water in the plants, so that sheep fed on them are liable to foot-rot, though the spring grass does not harm them.

The value of these water meadows may be realized by the fact that in chalk districts farmers possessing them keep the larger flocks ; moreover the certainty of the early feed makes it possible for lambing to take place soon after the turn of the year.

The cut and dried grass of all grasslands is known as hay, and this hay is sometimes further distinguished

[1] See page 12.

as meadow and upland hay ; it makes a very important winter food for sheep.

In haymaking the process of desiccation arrests fermentation, prevents the grass from becoming mouldy, and preserves the good feeding qualities of the green herbage. It is, however, of lower feeding value than grass in pasture, because older when cut than when grazed. The earlier the grass is cut, the higher the feeding value of the hay, but carefully dried hay is more nutritious than badly dried hay. A sound custom is to arrange the haymaking so that the longest day comes in the middle of hay time.

The five million acres of grass hay cut annually require much manual labour ; the modern introduction of machinery has greatly reduced this labour and improved the value by quickening the process, especially in rather sunless seasons. Hay-cutting by hand is done to-day only upon hill slopes or where the surface of the ground is irregular.

During haymaking the under surface of the swathes, windrows, or cocks is likely to become damp if the grass lie long unturned. To avoid this, the hay is sometimes tied into small sheaves and set up in stooks. Under ideal conditions the process of drying is somewhat as follows : after cutting, the swathes are broken up, shaken out over the entire surface of the field, and turned over from time to time. This last operation is called " tedding the hay ", and is usually effected by horse-drawn tedders ; the drying takes from four to five days. In southern England the hay lies on the ground till ready for carting ; elsewhere it is raked into windrows, wakes, cocks, pooks, etc., to await removal. In wetter districts the cutting for hay may have to be postponed till the weather becomes drier, but the quality of the herbage deteriorates if the grass become too old. Swathes can lie out in the rain for several days providing they are turned over if the under surfaces become yellow. The deterioration of half-made hay during rain is due to the leaching out of its valuable natural sap, the so-called " hay tea ".

To avoid injury through rain during the hay harvest northern farmers pile it into more or less cylindrical stacks pointed at the summit and contracted a little towards the base, so that much of the rain rolls off the stack.[1] When the cock has to be erected while the hay is still damp, it is opened in the daytime, spread out, and closed before night. Subsequently the cocks are taken to pieces and built into pikes or summer ricks still pointed at the top ; the ricks lie about the fields till the hay can be carted to the stack, which is often erected after the same pattern.

When the hay has been removed there may be a second crop of grass known as the aftermath, rowen, fog, foggage, or eddish ; it is inferior in food value owing to the lateness of the season, but can be used as hay for an early spring feed, thus cking out the winter stores. This aftermath may also be eaten fresh by young stock, which does not thrive on stale food, for example, on grass already depastured by sheep. The quality of the herbage is increased where this after-math is grown upon irrigated meadows.

The arable farming of Britain is said to be superior to that of most other countries and second to none, a pre-eminence gained through the intermixture of arable and pastoral farming. Many crops are produced under this system, but only the pastoral association will be considered here.

[1] In some parts of Scotland, e.g. Glencoe, the small stacks standing in the fields are protected from rain by a little canvas cap. They may also be netted for stability against wind.

During growth crops remove certain constituents of the soil, thus rendering it progressively less fertile. In good farming the agriculture is generally arranged to enable the soil to recover from this depletion. For example, nitrates make a useful plant food, and when removed by one variety of plant they may be returned by the growth of another. The bacteria that flourish in the nodules of the roots of leguminous plants seize upon and elaborate atmospheric nitrogen into chemical compounds which pass out into the soil; otherwise the deficient nitrogen may be supplied by the direct application of some form of manure, while different manures, animal or artificial, will make good different soil deficiencies.

To give the ground time to recover from the growth of a major crop before its next planting, various systems of " rotations " have been devised, involving the production of major crops, crops which keep down weeds, and crops for restoring fertility. The famous East Anglian or Norfolk four-course rotation is conducted as follows :

|  | Field A. | Field B. | Field C. | Field D. |
|---|---|---|---|---|
| 1st Year . . . | Wheat | Roots | Barley | Clover |
| 2nd Year . . . | Roots | Barley | Clover | Wheat |
| 3rd Year . . . | Barley | Clover | Wheat | Roots |
| 4th Year . . . | Clover | Wheat | Roots | Barley |

Roots, and particularly turnips, planted with a fair space between rows and individuals, are useful in keeping down weeds, for being strong growths they secure for themselves the major part of the plant food in the soil. The barley is sometimes mixed with clover and grass and harvested in autumn, the latter crops giving hay the following summer and an aftermath for grazing. The rotation clover may be replaced by beans, also nitrogen fixers, thus preparing the ground for bumper crops of wheat. The barley may need a chemical manure, but cow-shed manure is sufficient for roots. When superphosphates are given for turnips, and a complete fertilizer for mangolds, the three other courses usually need no other fertilizer, though a top dressing of sulphate of ammonia will benefit the barley, and even the wheat if the previous seed ley was predominantly rye grass.

There are several advantages of such a rotation. Each crop takes some different food from the soil, thus retarding special exhaustion. The work is distributed through the year ; after harvest the farmyard manure is carted to the land and the wheat sown. There are crops for the winter feeding of stock, the barley sowing takes place in spring, and in early summer the land is cleared for the planting of roots. The hay harvest and hoeing the roots follows, the corn harvest coming last. In addition, the interval between successive growths of the same crop gives opportunity for its particular pest to die, since in general these pests are peculiar to each species of plant. Moreover, when he can take up other harvests a partial or total ruin of any one crop is not absolute disaster to the farmer.

In the Central Lowlands of Scotland there is a six-coursed rotation of sequence, oats, potatoes, wheat, turnips, barley, grass, though there are also rotations including grasses three years in succession. On the other hand, the farmers of the English downlands are distinctly slack about rotations, probably because their often thin and poor soil supports grain crops with difficulty.

To provide for the livestock all the year round minor

crops are often run in between the main rotation crops, especially following corn. They are crops taken when opportunity arises, hence their name of catch crops. In this way a field will give two, three or even four harvests in any one agricultural year. These catch crops are either " fed off " the land, as described below, or provide a stall or fold feed. The autumn catch crops prevent the winter rain from washing away plant food from the soil ; some of them are known as " nitrate catchers ", among which mustard and quickly maturing turnips are notable. Some catch crops are grown to be ploughed in as green manure. Catch crops sown in summer and early autumn are designed for autumn feed ; those sown in late autumn for a spring and early summer feed. Spring tares (or vetches) are sown in early spring and where sheep farming is very important, if the land be available, catch crops may go in at almost any season.

The value of animal manure in arable farming is very considerable, and it may be applied directly to the ground by the simple process of folding sheep upon the arable or letting the livestock crop the roots either *in situ* or after they have been dug up and strewn on the land, or placed in feeding-troughs. In all these cases, by using hurdles the droppings of the farm stock can be arranged to give an evenly distributed manuring. It should be noticed that the catch crops assist to provide in one way or another for the main rotation crops.

Mustard and stubble turnips, put in after the corn is cleared, give an autumn keep ; turnips, swedes, or mangolds are ready by October, and as they require enormous storage and deteriorate by being kept, they are eaten during the winter, mainly by sheep and to a less extent by cattle. Autumn-sown catch crops for spring feed, when the roots have been consumed, are rye, winter barley, winter oats, winter tares, clovers, etc. The rye or winter oats can be fed green or made into hay with other grasses. Spring catch crops are less grown, as the land is required for the full main crop in the summer. They include spring wheat, spring tares, annual rye grass, trefoil. Rape and mustard, planted in spring for the summer feeding, and again in autumn, are catch crops on many chalk lands. Mustard is particularly useful for sheep fed on land infested with wire worms, which it helps to reduce. A catch crop of maize sown at the end of May or beginning of June, or after an autumn catch crop of rye, is grown in some districts.

Catch crops are more a feature of the farming in the southern than in the Midland counties of England, though they are very important in the south-east Midlands and East Anglia. Catch cropping requires a very long growing season and is practised where the climatic conditions are suitable and sufficient stock or sheep can be kept, or where some other early crops are not more profitable.

Arable farming is most prevalent where the rainfall is deficient for grass, and hence is chiefly practised in the eastern counties of Britain, though it holds a good place in the southern counties and in some other specially favoured districts.

Mixed farming in arable districts has the effect of producing food crops for livestock whose manure may be utilized for increasing the food production, to the further increase of the livestock production, and so on. This ideally increasing prosperity, however, has received some serious setbacks which will be discussed in detail later on. But though fewer livestock are now being kept as " arable livestock ", probably more cattle are being kept on arable land that has been seeded down

to grass.  Thus the mixed arable grassland farm is now
carrying more livestock but producing less dung.  On
the other hand, the post-war increase in potatoes and
sugar beet production has called for an enormous
demand for farmyard dung.

We must now consider a species of feeding ground
known as temporary pastures, or leys.  They are fields
deliberately sown with grasses and clovers of great
nutritive value for the feeding of farm stock.  These
" artificial pastures " may last for a year only, taking
their place in the local rotation.  For example, the
traditional four-course rotation may be varied slightly,
and grass seeds sown in spring-sown barley or with the
rotational clover give a " temporary pasture " as a
catch crop or a " rotational grass ".  On the other hand,
these pastures may have a longer life, designated short
or long leys, or more precisely one-, two-, three-, four-,
or five-year leys, after which they return to the rotation.
A four- or five-year ley will be getting somewhat weedy,
hence it is not carried on into a sixth year.

The chief plants involved in these temporary pastures
are clovers, trefoils, and other legumes, together with
various grasses known as " seeds ".  They are frequently
sown as mixtures ; sainfoin and lucerne sown separately
or in association with rye grass, trefoils, etc., also make
excellent leys for grazing or mowing.  The choice of
plant depends upon the anticipated life of the ley.
Thus the annual Italian rye grass is only useful in the
one-year ley, whereas the perennial white clover is
useful for both the one-year and longer leys.

In preparing a ley the seed is generally sown broadcast, the operation taking place in February if the sowing be on wheat, or even in April, May or June, if on
spring-sown crops.  This inter-sowing helps to keep
down weeds.  When the grain, etc., has been cut, the

ley seeds will be growing well, but if not very close together, trifolium or crimson clover can be added. Where the mixture produces a strong growth sheep can be run on the young plants, their feet pressing the soil round the roots and increasing their hold in the ground.

Leys with tall clovers and strong grasses can be cut green and handed out to cattle or sheep—this is known as soiling. Cattle should not be placed on leys where the soil is heavy or wet, for then they pull out the roots. Ten cuts can be taken from some clovers, and all clover pastures provide great stores of hay for winter feed. Clovers are also used for ensilage.

Unlike permanent pastures, leys occupy land kept under the plough. Apart from their feeding value to livestock, the manuring value of their clovers makes them of special utility in the farm economy.

In general, the drier the climate, the shorter the duration of the ley, though its life also depends upon such factors as the variety of seed selected, fertility of the soil, climate, and amount of the farm livestock kept. Since 1918 there has been a great increase of temporary pastures all over the country, especially in the counties of northern and south-western England and in Wales. These are areas of good rainfall, and the leys are generally long. In Surrey, Kent, and Sussex, on the other hand, the extent of the temporary pastures has suffered a distinct diminution.

## CHAPTER II

## MOUNTAIN SHEEP

THE mountain sheep include rather more than one-half the total number of sheep in Britain. They represent our oldest breeds, and though the different varieties have many qualities in common, probably because of the common factors that exist in the different environments, they show some distinct peculiarities individual to their special location. We shall consider in this chapter the mountain breeds occupying respectively the English Lake District, the Scottish Southern Uplands and the mountains of Wales.

The characteristic sheep of our Lake District is the silver-faced Herdwick, one of the hardiest of British breeds. The home of these sheep lies in the very heart of the Lakeland massif, among the highest hills of north Lancashire, Cumberland, and Westmorland, a country of exceedingly heavy rainfall, though where the steepness of the craggy and rock-strewn mountain pastures allows the water to run off swiftly the sheep keep perfectly healthy.

The breed is small, the rams are horned, the ewes polled or doddied, and the lambs, born almost black-faced, become gradually paler. The sheep grow thick and strong coats of close, but coarse, medium wool, which helps to keep them warm in winter. They have deep wide chests, and strong wide feet which grip and hold firm on bare or smoothed rock. They mature slowly ; on most high farms the ewes have their first lambs as gimmers, or two-year-olds, and sometimes

16

even later.  Twins are rare, and lambing, retarded by
the severity of the environment, does not take place
till April.  The pastures are of a wild moorland type,
with but scanty grazing, for moss, bare rock, and scree
abound, while in winter the snow often lies deep.  Succulent tufts of herbage sometimes tempt the Herdwicks
to dangerous climbs, stranding them in places from which
they are not liberated for some days, as their fear and
activity make it unsafe for the shepherd to attempt
rescue until they have been weakened by starvation.

Besides grass, the furze, whin, heather, juniper, fern,
and even holly of the moorland vegetation afford some
sustenance.  In times of famine the Herdwick will
descend to the farm and nibble the ivy on the walls.
The chief danger of the pasture is the snow, for all but
the young sheep and the lambing ewes spend the winter
upon the open fells.  If warned of the snow in time,
the shepherd and dogs will turn the flock to lower or
more sheltered slopes, or bring it into the dales, but
even when " snowed up " the sheep stand a good chance
of survival, for they huddle together in a cave of snow
thawed by their own warmth, and can live for weeks
upon the nutriment stored up in their own wool if
nothing else be available.  When the snow lies lightly
they scrape it away and so find their own grass.  Even
in the worst weather the Herdwick sheep is said to
refuse hay.

Owing to the severity of the winter the young sheep
are now sent to the lowlands for that season.  Walney
Island and the grasslands of the Cumberland coast
receive a great many.  Through the medium of the
papers lowland farmers offer for hire " good sound
wintering of Herdwick hoggs ", and the result is a great
congestion of sheep on the Lakeland routes in spring
and autumn.  The winterer must return all the lambs,

or their skins, and it is said the lambs often return only skins.

The fell farms consist of small holdings in the dale of not very productive land, and the farmers could not possibly do without the right, which goes with each holding, of common pasture on the fells.  Thus a little dale holding may control the heaf or hill slope behind it right up to the sky line, for a Herdwick sheep requires rather more than 4 to 5 acres for a year's keep.  A little " inland " walled off in the dale for the ewes in the lambing season helps out the annual grazing.

The fell pastures are mainly open commons, though there is some fencing.  Where there are walls a " hogg hole " gives passage, but the nimble Herdwick is quite capable of leaping any wall likely to be erected on the mountain-side.  The amount of straying, however, is not excessive, the sheep of each farm having for its heaf, fenced or unfenced, a great affection inherited from ancestors born and reared upon it.  For this reason it is impossible to sell the sheep from one farm to another near by—they would simply return.  Consequently the sheep are let with the farms—like the land, they belong to the landlord.  There is a certain amount of selling outside the region at the still existing ancient sheep fairs held at Eskdale, Ambleside, Kendal, Windermere and elsewhere, but occasions are known where the exiles, unguided and of their own accord, have made almost incredible journeys to return to their native heaf.  This return is sometimes prevented by tying together two legs of the leader of the exiled flock ; the rest then remain with their leader and become acclimatized to the new home.

In spite of this partiality for the home pasture, and the continuous patrolling of the shepherd and his dog, there is a certain amount of straying.  To cope with this each sheep is branded with a mark of ownership, and this mark is also recorded in the *Shepherds' Guide*, a publication of long standing. Upon certain days a general gathering of great antiquity, known as the "Shepherds' Meet", takes place, and the strays are brought hither to be identified and removed by their owners. These meets are held in summer or in winter at Mardale, Buttermere, Braithwaite, and elsewhere.

When the ewes have become old and broken mouthed, they are drafted from the stock and sold out of the region to lowland farmers.[1]

The characteristic sheep of the Scottish Southern Uplands and contiguous bordering highlands of England are the Scotch Blackface and the white-faced Cheviot.

The Blackface is the great sheep of the heathery parts of Scotland, keeping in best condition when it has to do much moving about to secure its daily ration of food. Its long and coarse wool protects it adequately from the rigours of its exposed habitat.

The Cheviot is the sheep of the grassy hills and dales, and probably native to the Cheviot ranges. Its wool is short and fine.

The hill pastures of Tweeddale breed both kinds of sheep. At one time its lower hills were covered with an open forest of oak, birch, and pine, but deforestation, sheep-grazing, the burning of heather and moorland grasses have transformed this country into grassland and heather moor. The hardy, horned Blackfaces occupy the higher, heathery portions, and the somewhat less hardy, hornless, white-faced Cheviots the lower grassy lands.

The farms of the Upper Tweed Basin are very large, being rarely of less extent than 1,000 acres, and often greater than 7,000 acres, the size limited only by the

[1] For their subsequent history see page 159.

C

amount of winter keep for the sheep. Before winter comes lambs are selected to replace the draft (five- or six-year-old) ewes, and the flock is brought up to its winter capacity by the sale of surplus sheep. In its winter quarters each Blackface ewe requires two acres of grazing, and four if the herbage be poor. Farm rents per acre are low, but vary with the quality of the farm pasture. The hill farms generally extend from some large stream to the watershed, and are almost entirely devoted to sheep. On account of its large size, the farm pasture is usually divided into divisions named *hirsels,* each with its own set of shepherds. Here, too, fences are rare, but the sheep keep to their own hirsel.

The average Blackface flock contains about 400 ewes, varying from ewe-lambs or hoggs of 6 months to the old ewes of 5 years. Such a flock would have seven to ten rams. The Blackfaces are averse to close flocking and may be seen devouring the heather on the hill slopes in little groups of three to ten individuals.

The sheep year begins in November. On high-level farms the sheep are sent to winter at lower levels from then till the new year, and the rams are put on the hills to run with the ewes. The sheep find the winter an exceedingly difficult time, for they generally procure their own food. In very stormy weather hay or turnips are given, and the sheep taken down to the lower lands. In times of winter stress, the Cheviot sheep require to be hand-fed sooner than the Blackfaces, who " work " with great energy. When supplied, the hay is scattered on the top of the snow, and may be blown about by the wind and trampled in by the sheep. Sometimes a double line of wire netting protects the hay, the animals getting at it through the meshes. Cake and corn are occasionally given in great emergencies, but the sheep will eat such food only if trained to do so when hoggs, and if not so

trained will die of hunger before touching it.  In storm
time the shepherd leads his flock to a *stell*, or circular
shelter of dry stones erected near a plantation if possible,
beside which is stored a reserve of bog or meadow hay.

The ewes begin to lamb at about two years of age ;
the lambing season starts about the third week in April,
the late date permitting a fair " bite " of grass on the
hill.  When in good condition the ewes are kind mothers ;
otherwise they have been known to refuse to own their
lambs.  The mortality among mothers and offspring is
rather high, owing to the weather and other adverse
circumstances ; twins occur rarely.  During the lambing
season the ewes range their customary pastures quite
freely, though some farmers devote one or two fields
at the bottom of each hirsel for the weakliest ewes,
those with twins, and for sick lambs, all of whom are
hand-fed, until they are sufficiently strong to return to
the hill.  The young lambs are usually very soon on
their feet.

Among their other uses, the stells shelter weak or
sick sheep at lambing time, and are called " keb-houses "
by the shepherds, a keb being a ewe who has lost her
lamb.  Such a ewe may be placed in the stell with a
lamb who is one of a twin, or who has lost its mother,
and here she remains till she consents to adopt the
lamb.  Often the lamb wears the skin of the dead one
in order to deceive the ewe.  At this season the shepherd
makes three rounds of the pastures each day—on
ordinary occasions he can attend to six or seven hundred
ewes, but about four hundred suffice him at lambing
time, when he is allowed the help of a lambing man if
that number be increased.

The next event in the pastoral year is the sheep
washing, which takes place about the last week in June,
and a week or ten days later the shearing begins, after

which the sheep are branded or otherwise marked for
identification. About the second week in July the hay
season sets in, when the farmer begins to lay up his
winter stores. The wool is largely sold at the wool
fairs that occur during this month and at other times,
and lambs and ewes not required to keep up the winter
flocks are sold in August, and rams in September, the
chief sale being at Hawick.

The mild climate and the excessive rainfall that beats
upon " the stormy hills of Wales " are responsible
directly and indirectly for the prevalence of its grass
and its widely extended pastoral industry. Excessive
and long-continued weathering of the ancient rocks
has produced a region of steep-sided ridges and peaks,
and narrow, precipitous upland glens ; these Welsh
Highlands are almost entirely surrounded by a fringe
of lowland of varying width, tongues of which are
carried as major river valleys into the heart of the hill
country. Whereas the grass of the higher region is too
short and wiry for modern cattle, the hardy mountain
sheep do excellently upon it, though here, as in the
Scottish Highlands, sheep were formerly of very much
less importance than cattle. The lower valleys support
some arable cultivation, mainly oats and sown grasses ;
there is also a high proportion of permanent grassland.
Upon the lowlands of Anglesey and the Lleyn Peninsula
this grassland is utilized for wintering sheep, a migration
which is not only necessitated by the climate but by
the sheep diseases (notably braxy) which attack the
young animals if they are not removed at this season
to the better climate and pastures of the coasts. The
remaining coastal lowlands of Wales are mainly devoted
to cattle.

The upland pastures, where grass predominates over
heather, support the sheep without fattening them,

whereas the lowland grass can provide them with good fattening pastures, hence the two complementary regions are linked by a species of pastoral solidarity. Ewes are bred on the hills, though they must come down to the lower farm lands for winter, while the lowlands, by means of the mountain ewes purchased from the hill, breed lambs which summer on the heights. The lowland farmer sometimes possesses rights of common pasture on the heights, thus being able to provide feeding grounds at both seasons, or he may have to purchase the summer grazing, just as the upland farmer may have to rent the winter keep. Where the sheep walks are not too elevated the wethers may be left up for the winter.

The farms in the valley or lower hill slopes are usually small and nearly all grass. They are generally worked by the farmer and his family, and though cattle are kept, often in large numbers, sheep are the chief asset.

The mountain sheep of Wales represent in the main two very ancient breeds ; the one, native to the highest hills, wild, dark-faced and horned ; the other, native to the lower hills, light or tan-faced. Both breeds are small, hardy and of slow growth, and give a mutton whose flavour is of the best. The sheep are wild and restless, and difficult to keep within fences ; they jump over walls with ease, though on the pastures a " sheep hole " is left for weaklings. Actually the loose stone walls of the Welsh upland pastures mark out the estates of the various ground landlords and hence may delimit fields several square miles in extent, though wire-fenced sheep walks, ranging from 400 to 2,000 acres, are also known. Where the owners of contiguous farms are tenants of the same proprietor, the sheep have every opportunity for mingling, but in practice they rarely wander far from their particular pitch. There is, of course, a certain amount of straying, but there is no *Shepherds' Guide* comparable to the Herdwick publication, and the return of strays is sometimes a matter of annoyance and difficulty. The sheep, however, appear to recognize when they are in the wrong, and intruders browsing on pastures sacred to some other flock quietly vanish when the home shepherd creeps among them after dark, and rattles stones in his pockets or flings about clods of turf. Though they remain with their comrades in the winter quarters without misgivings, they understand when they have been sold away from the flock. It is said that Glamorgan sheep sold to Brecknock sheep farmers will stand upon a hilltop looking homewards, and that when they sniff the south wind they set off forthwith, never pausing till they reach their old quarters.

Lambing time varies with the locality. In some parts of South Wales the flock is moved off the hills in October, and returns to them for lambing in April. Often the lambing takes place in the lower country, beginning about Christmas and lasting to the end of February. About April these young lambs accompany their mothers to the summer pastures, and remain with them till the end of June. The ewes are then shorn, branded for ownership, dipped in the stream, and then put out on the open common among the sheep of other owners.

# CHAPTER III

## SHEEP OF THE LOWER LANDS

WE shall now consider sheep-raising from the point of view of two contrasting types of pasture—arable and grass. At present arable sheep husbandry is suffering an eclipse, the winter fattening upon roots giving ground to a summer fattening upon grass, which may be local or only attained after a longer or shorter journey. The very intensive feeding on planted grasses and roots of the Hampshire and Wiltshire Downs has almost passed away, necessitating a change in the breed of sheep kept ; the reclamation of some ancient sheep walks for residential purposes, and the introduction of dairy-cattle and bullocks are other factors of the profound change in this area.

### THE ARABLE SHEEP—EAST ANGLIA

We assume here that the main purpose of the sheep-farming is to further the agriculture for which the soil is prepared by the growing of root and clover crops, sheep treading, and manure. The farm flock may include ewes and lambs for the breeding stock, and tegs and lambs for fattening, or it may consist of stock lambs only, or sheep kept merely for fattening, " flying flocks " being purchased each autumn and sold off every spring. The breeding stock clear the stubble after the harvest, and eat down the weeds, which, if unchecked, might later be troublesome. The sheep also clear up the corn from the harvest waste and the remainders after the better-favoured stock have been fed, a bite or bait of

25

turnip or mustard completing the diet. The ewe stock fares as sparsely as health will permit, while the young stock requiring sustenance for growth, or fattening, or both, spends its time in an untiring journey from one succulent pasture to another, the autumn-sown forage crops being somewhat as follows : winter rye, winter barley, crimson clover, tares, rape, cabbages, early turnips. The sheep are folded on the land by means of hurdles, and as the crops are consumed, the folds are moved elsewhere, the ground cleansed, and drilled with mangold, rape, swedes, and turnips. Clover and sainfoin hay give cut fodder, and on some farms cotton and linseed cake and other concentrates are largely fed to the fattening stock, the richness of the resulting manure compensating in part for the increased feeding expenses.

During the winter period previous to lambing the ewes, if close folded, are exercised daily for a short time, but since on an arable farm continuous cropping can always be arranged, lambing is made to take place as the market dictates. February and March are good periods, weaning then taking place in June, but lambs can be born in September to supply the early fat lamb market.

When the lambing season has arrived the ewes are removed to permanent or temporary folds, and after the birth, mother and lamb retire to another pen for a few days, during which the ewe is fed on roots. When sufficiently recovered, she spends her day in the open fields, returning at night to her pen after an evening meal of roots, hay, and corn.

As soon as the lambs are able to do so, they go with the ewes to the fields, taking refuge at need in hurdle shelters. During the fourteen or fifteen weeks while the ewes are still suckling their lambs, they receive a generous diet of oats, peas, decorticated cotton or linseed cake, dried grains, ensilage, roots, etc., in addition to what they pick up in the fields.  The food is given in troughs or strewn about, the couples being confined by hurdles to definite parts of the field.  When a new portion is to be attacked, the lambs run forward through lamb creeps in the hurdles (lamb-hurdles) to get the first bite at the fresh food.  The troughs and hurdles are so arranged daily that the manure or droppings are distributed about the field as uniformly as possible. In June the lambs are weaned.

After the weaning the ewes are washed and shorn, and having relinquished their lambs return to the poor feeding already mentioned.  In and after October they receive a liberal allowance of hay, and their diet is also temporarily increased for a month or so at ram-time, and just before lambing.

The first food of the young lamb is ewe's milk, though in emergency the babies may have to be fed from a bottle with cow's milk.  As soon as possible the lambs are enticed to take some artificial food in the shape of finely ground linseed cake, pea mash, etc.  This food is put in troughs apart from the hurdled enclosed area where are the ewes, the lambs going through the lamb creeps, as already described.  If not required for the breeding stock, 12-days' old male lambs are castrated, and all are docked, the latter operation removing the discomfort of dirty tails.  As the ewe-milk falls off the lamb is given some water and a lick of salt from a block put in the fold.  After weaning the lambs (on the ideal farm) are removed to good clean pastures, stale ones being apt to give them diseases.  The arrangements for trough feeding and pasture continue, except that the lambs are now without their mothers.  The enclosures may be marked off by fences of wattles or slatted hurdles, or of wire, or netting, though the sheltering property of the hurdles makes them the best form of fencing.  The young lambs are washed and dipped or plunged up to their necks in a bath of some disinfectant solution to reduce the biting by injurious flies : they are not always shorn at this time.  During autumn the lambs are run on stubble and young seeds, rape or cabbage, with white turnips as a night feed.

In winter the lambs go to the farm buildings, spending their days in yards and their nights in sheds, either open or covered.  The winter feed is still succulent and various—kohlrabi, corn, hay, chaff, are given in troughs, and when this is eaten the troughs are filled with sliced roots till the animals are satisfied and move away to rest. About noon they get a second meal of roots, and at dusk corn and then roots, after which the troughs are filled for a night feed.  This fattening process goes on from November to April.

The fattening of tegs is a summer or winter occupation.  In summer fattening the lambs are one-year-olds, and are kept on grass, oats, cake, etc.  They are shorn and drafted to market as they become ready.  For winter fattening they are purchased at winter fairs if not of the home flock, and are placed on rape, turnips and swedes in turn, and finally the full winter keep. They may have a daily run on grass, old aftermath, and a small allowance of corn, after which they are confined between hurdles or nets and feed on swedes with an increasing amount of cake, corn, and hay.  About January or February the tegs are sold when fattened, and this may give sufficient time for a second stock of tegs or lambs in forward condition to be bought in and fattened for sale before or after shearing.

### GRASS SHEEP WITH A LITTLE ARABLE

This type of sheep husbandry is practised in a number of the eastern counties, the main object being the production of fat lamb. The sheep are reared in districts where there are few catch crops available in spring, but where roots and grasses from the agricultural rotation help out the permanent pasture grass of which there is, however, a considerable amount. The lambing season is therefore late (never before March) so that the ewes can, at this time, obtain a good " bite " from this grass.

The ram is put to the ewe during the second week in October, and from this time until lambing the ewes feed on the stubbles and leys, with turnips in December, and clean up the fattening pastures when the lambs have taken the first toll. A few weeks before and after lambing they go wholly on the pastures with some trough feeding such as turnips, before the lambs are born, and a better supplement of roots (mangolds), corn, or cake at the farmer's discretion after. There is also folding of the couples on grass or clover leys with the lamb creeps in the hurdles described in connection with the more purely " arable " sheep, and similar too are the other details of lambing, docking, shearing, dipping, etc.

After weaning the lambs, now known as tegs, feed upon fresh clover aftermath, etc., and cabbage and turnips in addition, until winter. The lambs spend much time on the grass to get ready for the butcher. The draft ewes are fattened on mustard, rape, and grass ; in the Lincoln Fens the rape grows higher than the hurdles, and the sheep eat both the leaves and stems of the growing plant.

The flocks consist of ewes, lambs, store or fattening tegs or wethers : the price paid for the fleeces results in there being fewer lamb sales in the early winter— more are fattened out as shearlings and sold largely at spring fairs for fattening on the rich Fen pastures.

More highly bred flocks intended for shows and early sheep sales receive kale, kohlrabi, cabbage and additional rye, tares, cake, and corn.

### GRASS SHEEP WITH NIGHT FOLDING ON ARABLE

The scarplands of south-eastern England contain many geological formations. Where there are superficial gravel deposits upon the chalk the pasture is very rough, and gorse abounds. Sometimes the chalk is covered with clay-with-flints, and the soils derived from it contain very little or no free lime. If the natural drainage of the soil is good it can carry very fair pastures, but if the natural drainage is poor or the soil is sour it gives rise to patches of damp oak wood or damp pastures for sheep or cattle when the wood has been cleared. The actual soil of the chalk is thin and light, requiring additional organic matter to keep it fertile, and the age-long manuring and treading by sheep has resulted in much of it becoming capable of an intensive arable farming. Crops relished by sheep have long been grown upon it, thus preparing for an augmented fertilization and bumper harvests of grain or roots for human consumption. The hoof of the sheep here has been pure gold.

However, it is just these southern chalk lands of intensive agriculture that are to-day largely " tumbling down " to grass, so that though some flock masters retain the traditional " chalk " animals, others are using special sheep breeds and crosses more suitable to the new conditions, while others are putting on dairy cows owing to the increasing demand for milk and excellent transport facilities.

Some of the chalk soil has never been suitable for ploughing, either because of its infertile character, or high elevation, or both. Here there are pastures of short, wiry grass, traditionally the realm of the sheep, and where they still feed during the day time, though they are folded upon neighbouring arable at night. This arable was once bare fallow, and the sheep received but a meagre sustenance in return for their manure, but in time root crops were grown upon this fallow, inducing the sheep who consumed them to give a richer manure, so that the ground could support some catch cropping.

We shall take our example from the Sussex Downs, where the traditional method of sheep-rearing is still in operation.

We may begin the ewe's year with the lambing time. The lambing may take place on the open field, but more usually, as hay is required for litter, food, etc., the lambing folds are erected near a haystack.

After the early tail-docking ewes and lambs are turned out freely on the hill, the ewes often wearing bells whose ringing enables their lambs to find them. A sheep dog keeps an unceasing supervision over their welfare, rounding the sheep up at night, and driving them into the folds through holes in the hurdles. After weaning time the lambs and ewes are separated, the latter being deprived of their bells and shorn. The ewes now roam the hills by themselves, still guarded by the dog, who, at a sign from the shepherd, drives them from one piece of pasture to another, or makes them finish up a piece of pasture only partially consumed and which they would fain neglect for a feed more attractive. The so-called dew ponds of the higher grounds supply much of the drinking water, and thither the ewes are driven by the dog at the appropriate time. The shepherd follows the flock at a little distance, noting truants and sending the dog after strays. As they enter the night fold the shepherd takes a tally. In the morning the ewes return to the down pastures—their daily journeys between fold and pasture are sometimes quite considerable.

When the lambs have been weaned, they are folded apart from the ewes. In September a pen is fixed near the fold and such lambs as are not required for the breeding stock are prepared for sale. A kind of forked stick, known as "bows", is driven into the ground thus : Y, the head of the lamb is pushed into it, secured by a bolt and covered with a sack while the rest of the body is brushed and trimmed. Two days later the lambs are driven across the Downs and over the green trackways and dusty roads to the fair-ground, a journey which may be considerable. On arrival the lambs are packed into pens, and there remain all day without shelter, food, or water. After sale another shepherd and dog take them to the railway, where they entrain for their winter quarters and subsequent fattening for the spring or summer slaughter.

### GRASS FED SHEEP OF THE MARSHES

Our example will be taken from the sheep of Romney Marsh, or " Kent " sheep, whose habitat includes the Romney Marsh and other low marshes within the county.

The Romney Marshes consist of an alluvial plain, mainly of clay, but diversified with patches of sand and gravel. The plain is very flat, with open draining ditches every 5 or 6 yards. In addition to the usual marsh plants of yellow iris, sedges, reeds, etc., a very rich grass grows upon the fertile alluvium giving excellent sheep pasture whose value is enhanced by the presence of salt. The regional rainfall is rather heavy, while the absence of trees and the general flatness aggravate the effects of the cold north and east winds of the severe winter and spring.

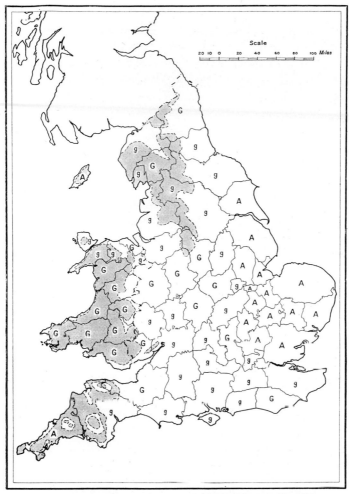

### ARABLE CULTIVATION AND PERMANENT GRASSLAND

Counties where arable cultivation predominates over permanent grassland are marked A. Counties where permanent grassland predominates over arable cultivation are marked G (where acreage of permanent grassland is at least three times the acreage in arable), or g (where the proportion is less). Shaded areas indicate where the annual rainfall is 40 inches or more.

As a rule *cattle* rather than sheep are associated with a marsh pasture, as sheep suffer from foot-rot when on a damp lair.  The Romney Marsh sheep, however, have apparently acquired immunity from this disease, possibly through a process of survival of the fittest operative over many generations ;  possibly on account of the efficient draining of the ground between the ditches, and the brackishness of the water, such water being hostile to the liver-fluke at one period of its existence. Actually the sheep population of Romney Marsh is greater than that of any other country of equal area, and in summer one acre of the rich grass suffices for twelve two-hundred-pound wethers or six to eight fattening sheep and lambs.  Even so, the grass is not entirely eaten up, and bullocks are often kept upon the Marsh from May till September, so that it may be properly grazed.  The sheep fatten without additional food.

The draining ditches confine the sheep to definite areas, so that the pasture does not become soiled by overcrowding in any one part, though actually these sheep are not very gregarious, and spread themselves out as evenly as possible over their available pasture. The grass is thus free from the taint of the concentrated droppings that occur when sheep feed in a bunch.

The Romney Marsh sheep is a large, hornless, white-faced " Roman-nosed " sheep, with a thick, closely-curling fleece of long wool.  The older sheep are sufficiently hardy to winter in the open, but as the grass at this season is much less nourishing than in summer, an acre of pasture will only take two to three ewes.  The Marsh is too wet and bleak to winter the young sheep, and there is a general exodus of them at the end of July or in August for the uplands of Kent, Sussex, and Surrey.  The transit is made on foot or by rail, according to distance, and for a month or so the bleating of the ovine troops fills the countryside. The lambs spend the winter as stores, to be sold as hoggets at two years old.[1] The upland farmers to whom they are agisted [2] receive some payment for the grazing they supply of stubble or grattons (Kentish) or poor pasture. Some of the Marsh farmers possess upland farms, where their lambs may get good grass and hay ; other farmers, if paid additionally, give cake and corn. In high-grade flocks many lambs winter in the fold, getting rape and mustard, turnips and swedes as the winter goes on. But the poorer fare is the general rule, and lambs not infrequently return to the Marsh in a very emaciated condition, while the winter mortality is about 10–20 per cent.

The return to the Marsh takes place in April, the lambs coming back as one-year-olds or tegs (Romney nomenclature). The small number of ewes agisted to distant farms return likewise for lambing, which the April weather permits to take place in sheltered enclosures near the homestead or in temporary pens in the open. The night feed for the ewe at this time is hay and perhaps turnips, but care is taken to pamper neither ewe nor lamb, since the latter in due course will have to undergo the hardships of the Marsh.

While on the Marsh the flocks are supervised by a few " lookers ". The ewes graze away from their lambs, joining them from time to time.

The shearing takes place in May and early June, mechanical shearers being in general use. This operation helps to keep down the fly or sheep maggot,

[1] The Romney Marsh nomenclature is slightly different from that in use elsewhere.

[2] In England and Wales the seasonal exile of the sheep is known as agistment. The seasonal keep, during the agisting, must be paid for.

though in very wet winters the shorn lamb suffers from the loss of its natural covering; the shorn ewe is of hardier constitution. The rams are turned out about the middle of October and remain with the ewes for two months; 25–30 per cent doubles, or twins, are by no means rare.

The Romney Marsh flocks are exceptionally large for British sheep, a Marsh flock-master owning some thousands of animals. Lamb sales take place on the outskirts of the Marsh towards the end of August, when such lambs are disposed of as it is not intended to agist.

For an account of the more intimate details of the lambing, marking, shearing and other operations of the sheep year, the reader is referred to Chapter XIX. In this chapter we are mainly concerned with the geographical aspect of sheep-rearing; for example, the influence of soil and climate upon the growth of forage crops and pasture grasses, how these may influence the time of lambing, etc. " Cultivated " vegetation may be regarded as geography no less than the " natural vegetation " that looms so largely in our text-books, and at least gives us a clue to the work that goes on in the farming regions.

D

## CHAPTER IV

## THE DAIRY HERD OF BRITAIN

OUR account of the sheep-rearing industry was based upon the geographical environment in which it is carried on, but this plan cannot be used to quite the same extent with regard to cattle. The great size of cattle and the good quality of the food they need mark them out more particularly as the animals of the lower lands. " The cow," wrote a child in an essay upon the subject, " is a solemn animal ; it does not skip about like some young lambs do," and though the truth of this criticism is perhaps a little doubtful, cows are not, in fact, the denizens of our wilder " top lands " whereon the more agile sheep may " skip " delightfully.

In this chapter we shall consider the British Dairy Herd in a general way, and follow up the output in calves to the pastures appropriate to their destination in life.

In the British Isles it is the custom to adopt special methods of rearing and feeding where cattle are specifically intended for meat production, while in Europe, apart from the intense market for veal, the more usual process is to rear cattle for milk or field-labour, and defer fattening for the meat market until their utility in these respects has come to an end. Hence, although cattle-rearing with meat as its sole object is making its way in certain favourable parts of Europe, in general, unless the meat is sufficiently young to pass for veal, it is decidedly " old " meat.

It has been estimated [1] that something like 3·6

[1] Wood and Newman, *Beef Production in Great Britain*.

million calves are produced yearly by the British Dairy Herd. Of these about ·8 million calves of under one year are killed for veal, 1 million put aside to make up the annual wastage in the general herd, 1·3 million fattened and killed as prime beef at two years old or more, about 300,000 killed at eighteen months old as " baby beef ", and the remaining 200,000 or so die as the result of diseases or mishaps, or are required for bulls and the export of livestock. The million or so dairy cows discarded annually in their turn, are fattened for the meat market. In Britain certain breeds of cattle are known as " dual purpose "—the cows of such breeds give good milk ; the males, unwanted females and the discarded dairy cows, on fattening, make good meat.

Cattle breeding and the rearing of animals for milk or meat take place, of course, all over the country, but our present concern is with those large areas whose geographical qualities make cattle-rearing for one particular branch of the industry the more natural process. The grass of the rich clay vales of the English Midlands suffices to fatten cattle without undue additional expense, whereas much of the permanent grass pastures of the north and west will not do this without considerable outlay in artificial foods, though it is quite suitable for cattle in the store condition, when they are merely growing and building up the framework upon which the flesh can afterwards be laid. On the other hand, in arable districts where grass acreage is small or where the limited natural pastures are required for other purposes, vast stores of forage can be produced, which forage, with or without the help of artificial food, can be used to fatten the beasts in their stalls ; the resulting manure, as in the case of sheep, would be devoted to associated and other agricultural needs. This " arable fattening " is expensive, and the main profit consists in the manure produced.

The natural grasslands of Wales, the West Country, Ireland, and the uplands of Scotland provide a suitable pasture for our young calves in the store stage up to 2-2½ years old.  Even in summer the quality of the herbage is such that to satisfy their appetite the animals must eat much and roam far.  This search for the daily food also uses up a great deal of the bodily energy, so that part of the food eaten repairs waste rather than adds to growth.  In winter the pastures are at their worst, and the stores receive some hay, a bulky food and here of inferior quality, so that again the appetite is satisfied without a great amount of nutriment having been consumed.  Under these conditions the animals grow but slowly.  The free life of the animals on the pastures does not require much supervision.  When the winter is not too severe the stores spend all the year in the open.  In North Wales, where the winter is very bleak, they are driven to the lee of a mountain during bad weather, or take refuge by night in rough covered shelters constructed of the local stone, or wooden stakes and furze.  In no case are the running expenses great, so that, with the good prices obtained for stores required for fattening, there is a considerable margin of profit.

The stores of Central Wales are very useful grazers for the summer pastures of the English Midlands.  These " Welsh runts " are big-framed and of a hardiness that produces quick results when they are brought to the luscious grasslands of the Midlands.  The stores are despatched to the fattening districts as soon as they are ready by age or size, but the process of transfer is somewhat involved, for in general the store farmer is not in the position to find his fattening market.  During their passage from the breeding to the fattening districts,

the cattle change hands several times, the operation
being somewhat as follows :

When the stores are ready local dealers buy small
lots at the local fairs and markets, or direct from the
farms ; stores to be fattened on grass in the Midlands
begin to be bought in spring, and those to be " finished "
on roots, etc., in the autumn.  The local dealers take
these stores to what may be regarded as a sort of half-way
market for store cattle, located somewhere between the
breeding and fattening districts.  Here they meet the
dealers from these latter districts, who buy and remove
the stores to these districts.  A third sale now takes
place, whereby the stores are retailed to the various
farmers for finishing.  The expenses of transit, including droverage, rail journey, dealers' profits, market dues,
and so on, are great, and great too is the fatigue of the
animals during this journeying.

The fattening industry of the Midland grasslands is
a summer industry, due, in part, to the particular
density of the herbage at this season, which permits the
animals to satisfy their appetites without much expenditure of energy in securing their daily bite.  The uniform
rate of growth of this grass encourages heavy stocking,
so that the sward is kept closely grazed and is eaten
over when quite young, that is, when its feeding quality
is at its maximum.  In about twelve or fourteen
weeks the animals are ready for slaughter, and a second
consignment is brought to the pastures also for fattening, though some cake and other artificial foods must
be given to help out the now slightly failing grass.  The
cattle spend all their time out of doors, and special
supervision is devoted to seeing that highly fed animals,
particularly active in July, do not leap their fences
and break bounds.  During September the animals are
removed as they become sufficiently fattened, the

meadows thus gradually carrying less stock.  If they are not all ready by the end of the month, they must be stall-finished on turnips, clover, hay, and oil-cake.

Fattening in the arable counties is a winter process. The younger and smaller stores are housed in boxes or in covered or partly covered-in yards well littered with straw.  The more comfortable and sedentary the creatures are the less they move about, thus lessening the tissue waste, so that practically all the food that is not returned as manure is used to build up flesh. Scotch feeders are particularly adept in this arable fattening, and though much English beef is equal to the best of the Scotch, the generality of the latter decidedly holds the palm for goodness.  The feeding given is cake, meal, roots (cut, pulped, or steamed), and hay chaff.  The animals are sold in early spring as they become ready, and probably all are gone by the end of June.  The stalls are re-filled, the diet now generally including green food, tares, clover, Italian rye grass, lucerne and mangolds, till the animals have been broken in to the stall feeding, when rape, or cotton seed cake, or meal and chaff are added.

The littered straw makes a very excellent manure, owing to the decomposition it undergoes in the stall or dung-heap ; it also helps the soil particles to form a mulch.  During winter feeding an animal may provide as much as 8 tons of manure, a valuable asset for light soils growing large quantities of roots.

This East Anglian industry has of late undergone rather drastic changes.  Formerly intense fattening of the older stores produced the large joints of the traditional " prime Christmas beef ".  The present propensity for smaller joints has resulted in a winter feeding, but not fattening, of young bullocks on roots, the animals being finished later upon the summer grass.  However,

much Christmas beef is still entirely stall-fed, and stall-
finished young bullocks are still produced for the
Christmas market.

It has been noticed that animals may be reared and
fattened in the same area.   Stores may be kept in yards
in the arable districts with a winter feed of roots (cut or
pulped) and hay, and straw and chaff, with perhaps some
cake.   Many arable farms contain some meadowland,
which can be utilized as summer pastures, or even right
up to December may receive store cattle for a few hours'
outing daily.

On the South Downs there is some store-raising
subsidiary to the main sheep-raising industry ;  bullocks
purchased in autumn spend the winter in " lodges "
high on the hill-slopes, and are fed on oats, straw, seeds,
hay and roots, all crops produced in the arable districts
of the chalklands.   They are sold in spring as forward
stores.   In the Carse lands of Forfar[1], Irish stores are
fattened on grass during the summer with the help of a
little cake.   The amount of good permanent cow pasture,
however, is not great, and only to be found at the foot
of the hills.   As the season advances more bullocks are
bought in, started on grass, and generally drafted into
yards to be finished.   Here heavy cake feeding is usual.

The Pevensey Level is another district that should be
particularly noticed.   Composed of Wealden clay, it
produces a somewhat coarse herbage which is nevertheless of great feeding value.   It is chiefly grazed by
fattening bullocks, many of whom come, as stores, from
the neighbouring Sussex Hills, but in still greater
numbers from Ireland and Devon.   Devon stores are
also popular stock for fattening in the Sussex corn-belt,
Chichester being a well-known market for these stores.
The animals trample down the straw and are fed in yards,

[1] See footnote, p. 99.

though some farmers have grassland upon which they can be fattened if a little cake be also given.

The fattening of discarded dairy cows is a small industry. In October London cow-keepers remove them from the herd, feed them well on turnips, hay or oat chaff, meal or oil-cake, till they cease to give milk, and then send them to the butcher.

The British Dairy Herd has no special location, as in the case of stores and fattening stock. Where grass is sufficiently good for milch cows, and home farms or pastures in touch with the requisite transport facilities, the production of milk for local or distant needs will be a profitable industry. Where districts otherwise suited to dairying are rather inaccessible to profitable markets for the liquid milk, this latter, after supplying family or local needs, will be worked up into a better keeping commodity such as butter or cheese, which may also be the product of the summer excess in districts supplying milk all the year round.

The management of the dairy cow depends upon the climate and food resources to hand. As an example of grass-fed cows, we may take the milk-producing districts of Ayrshire and Wigtownshire. Here the cows feed entirely on grass from May to October and, but for two visits a day to the byres for milking, are out on the pastures all day and night. From October to May the animals are still kept in the open, but they are housed in the byres at night during the depths of winter. The "winter grass" offers but poor nutriment, and is supplemented with large quantities of straw, turnips, swedes and small amounts of meal, cake, and oats. In cheese dairies milking ceases in early winter, and calving takes place in early spring, so that the best grass food is ready when most required. In milk dairies the calving takes place at all seasons, since the supply of milk must be kept up throughout the year. The bull calves are slaughtered soon after birth.

On arable farms sufficient material is at hand to give the cow, previous to calving, good feeding of hay, straw, chaff, pulped roots, cake, etc., and in addition brewers' grains—which can easily be purchased, and which mitigate the dryness of the chaff—bran, a fine milk food, rice meals and other fat producers such as malt culms, roots and grains. Cows are generally taken from the fields for yard feeding during winter, receiving the usual diet of roots, meal, chaff and straw. In summer they should have grass pastures, additional cut grass being supplied in the early summer and again towards autumn. The night is spent in stalls or sheds, with a night feed of roots, grains, cake, hay, and often cabbage. Town-fed cows receive hay, roots, and concentrates in winter, and brewers' grains, cabbages, cut tares and clovers in summer.

The calving time is arranged so that the dairy farm or district can supply milk all the year. The new-born calf receives its mother's milk (the rich colostrum) for a few days, and then new and finally skimmed milk; it should be induced to eat as soon as possible. A wisp of fresh hay is sometimes hung up within reach, and the calf enticed to nibble at it. As the supply of milk fed to the calf decreases, the amount of trough food (oat chaff, barley, straw, early turnips) increases. Young calves are often put out to grass by day and housed and trough-fed in yards at night, while towards autumn, when the turnips are beginning to be stored for winter use, fresh carrots and swede tops are useful. Some farmers do not put their young calves out to grass, considering that they get chills in winter and are upset by sunshine and flies in summer; others advocate shady pastures. It is claimed that calves,

and even cows, will starve in the shade rather than
move out to feed in sun-glare. Our mildish winters,
however, allow grazing to continue until late autumn,
and many calves winter entirely on grass or are put
out on the pastures in spring. The winter yarding of
young stock is effected on stored food—hay, straw,
chaff, roots, and some concentrates. The calves should
be associated in little groups of not more than eight or
twelve, and all the members of one group should be
about the same age. Otherwise there is trouble at
feeding time, the stronger ones horning the younger or
less assertive away from the feeding trough.

Perhaps an excuse is necessary for the somewhat
frequent lists of feeding materials that have been given
in this chapter. The intention is to indicate the great
importance of the arable farming associated with the
pastoral industry.

# PART II
## THE ANCESTRY

# CHAPTER V

## BEGINNINGS IN UPPER BRITAIN

THE distinction between Upper and Lower Britain was made by the Romans to mark the highland, or less civilized portion of the country, from the lowland, over which the Great Nation held a very detailed control. The line of demarcation is the 500-foot contour, still useful in differentiating our uplands and lowlands. In this chapter we shall select typical modes of pastoral life from the Highlands of Scotland and Wales, and the Southern Uplands of England.

Scotland contains much unproductive moor and bog land diversified by fertile straths or wide valleys. In the earlier times the Highlands were pre-eminently the domain of the cattle, a small, black, hardy race, with curiously long horns. The lairds kept them in great numbers, and practically every cottager had a few cattle, because of the value of the milk and dung. Some goats and sheep were also kept, the latter giving the fine, rather scanty wool, worked up as the family homespun.

The laird as ground landlord rented out much of his estate to the tacksman, who kept the best lands for his own farming, sub-letting the rest in farms taken over by three or four tenants in joint occupancy. The cottars were labourers on these farms; they possessed a cow or two and a few sheep together with a piece of ground for growing some foodstuff. Their masters gave them fuel and a little meat, and sufficient free time to look after their own farming.

47

The general custom was to divide the farm territory into an in-field and an out-field, the former occupying the lower and more accessible site.  The in-field was broken up into ridges which were cultivated by the different farmers of the group.  The strips were allotted yearly, care being taken that the poorer holdings did not fall to the same individual twice in succession. This practice of field cultivation was known as the *run-rig*.  The cultivation followed a more or less definite rotation built upon an original system of two crops of oats, one of barley, and a fallow.  The barley was sometimes of the inferior quality known as bear, and sometimes peas made part of the rotation.  Barley land was ploughed up two or three times during the winter, but oat land only once, just after the harvest or before the sowing.  The whole of the farmyard manure was given to the barley.  Often, before use, this manure was mixed with sods and the old thatch and divots taken from the dwellings.  Manuring was done before sowing, and after the harvest the cattle wandered at will over the stubble, thus giving a second, but unsystematic, manuring.

The out-field, consisting of grass and weeds, was sometimes at a considerable distance from the farm.  It was fertilized by the method of tathing, that is, folding the animals at pasture upon a piece of ground walled in by sods and earth.  The fold was occupied during the night and at noon for a period lasting from eight to ten days, when it was moved on.  As soon as a good-sized piece of land had become sufficiently fertilized, it was ploughed up and put under crops of oats and barley for three or more consecutive years till exhausted, the final crop of " rush " oats being only fit to feed cattle unthreshed.  The soil was now left to weeds and thistles for three or four years more—or even eight years—when folding was resumed and the process repeated.

The means described above, of feeding the farm stock, were rarely sufficient, and additional pasturage was utilized in grassy glens often very far from the district they served. These glens, browsed over by the cattle and sheep of the community " in common ", were the *shielings*, a name more particularly applied to the huts occupied in summer by the portion of the family that accompanied the cattle, sheep, and goats to these summer pastures. The farm rent included use of this pasture, which was the more important as quite two-thirds of the hill grazings were unfit for cattle. The summer journey to the shieling was often a long one ; the cattle roamed the shielings at will, with some supervision against straying, and the sheep and goats were generally penned at night. The return took place at the end of August or the beginning of September ; it was generally reckoned that the summer feeding produced good beef, since by the end of spring the cattle had so little flesh on their bones, that the summer increase might almost be ranked as " new flesh ". Since bullocks were not slaughtered till four or five years old, the farmer had to keep up a regular succession of young beasts, each cow having as progeny on the farm a calf, a one-year-old, a two-year-old, and a three-year-old. When the farmer had selected the animals he wished to keep through the winter, the rest were sent to the local markets. On their return home the cattle and sheep to be wintered were put upon bare stubble and open fields, where they picked up what they could, all the stock of one district " eating promiscuously ". They usually spent the winter out of doors, some rough shelter being provided in stormy districts. The sheep were often tethered, and always received hay. A certain number of young beasts belonging to the chief tenant or laird were stall-fed or wintered by the sub-tenants as part payment of rent arrears, when the straw of last year's grain and some rush oats were all the food given except in some districts, where a little hay, garnered while the animals were at the shielings, made a welcome addition.    After a hard winter it was generally necessary to carry the emaciated cows out of the cow-shed to fresh pastures, the low condition of these stall-fed cattle being such that calving could take place only every other year ;    barely four-fifths of the outdoor stock survived the winter.

Life for the sub-tenants oscillated between a strenuous summer and an inactive winter.    In general, the cottages were mere hovels of stone and feal (that is, turf and sod), the floor of trodden earth and the roof of thatch with an aperture to serve as chimney.    The family hearth occupied a little enclosed parapet below this outlet, and over it swung a kettle suspended by a hook and chain, while hanging mutton, bathed in the all-pervading smoke, underwent a slow cure.    Resinous splinters of fir wood, often partly fossilized, supplied the only illumination beyond that admitted by the open door and the roof hole.    The family lived at one end of the apartment, the cows and young stores at the other, there being no partitions, and all, humans and animals, used the same door.    The " beasties " supplied some of the needed heat.    The monotony of the winter days was sometimes broken by the incursions of foxes, who took large toll of sheep and lambs.    Most districts boasted a fox-killer, paid for collectively by the community.

After the spring ploughing and sometime in May, a move was made to the summer pastures.    The main body of males remained at the farm, or at any rate put in the necessary work at its agricultural labours.    The women and children and a few of the older men went with the animals to the shielings. Most important amongst the little company was the head herdsman of the shieling and the milkmaids. This migration, known as the *glaning*, was to the grassiest and most sheltered glen on the holding. Cattle, ewes and goats were driven along in front, and behind came carts laden with blankets, foodstuffs, churns, dishes, etc., with the old women of the community and their spinning wheels on top, while barking dogs asserted their authority as directors and protectors of the procession. During the summer, supplies of butter and cheese were prepared, and there were such recreations as fish and game could provide for those able to enjoy them. The men of the community came and went between the shieling and the " winter home ", where they attended to such tillage as there was. The women found recreation in " wanking the cloth ", a toilsome process, but accomplished with the aid of much singing. On the shieling also a sharp look-out was kept for foxes, whose natural homes lay in the heather. The shieling dwellings were of turf, or turf on a stone foundation. Beds were made of heather. When the grass had been pretty well grazed and the days were becoming short and the weather bad, the return was made to the farm, where the work of the harvest was taken in hand.

This system of farming provided for nearly all the needs of the Highland community—milk, cheese, butter, and meat for the family table, leather for brogues and harness, wool for clothing, horns for spoons and drinking vessels, and rent payments out of the sale of the cattle. Towards the close of the eighteenth century this traditional mode of life received its death-blow by the introduction of large-scale sheep-farming Particulars of this invasion will be given later.

E

We now pass on to cattle and sheep keeping in the Highlands of Wales.

In the early centuries the wind-swept headlands and hill-tops of Wales bore grass or grass-heath, the rest of the territory being covered with forest. The general mild climate and high precipitation with corresponding lack of sunshine must from the first have marked out the high Welsh moors as Nature's pasture lands, while the narrow and deeply cut valleys which dissect them provided sheltered places for cultivation.

It has been supposed that the earlier inhabitants of these highlands were moorland communities engaged in stock-keeping. After the introduction of grain they appear to have forsaken their moorland homes and, descending the slopes to shelves above the steep declivities, taken up their abode there under a somewhat patriarchal system by means of which a family group became the nucleus for a village. The old piece of moorland or hill-top patch still gave common pasture for the stock of those households formerly associated with it, and valley bottoms still lower gave opportunity for grain and meadow-grass (hay) cultivation. This mode of life implied a summer residence on the high pastures for at least some or all of the family, as the meat consumed by the peasantry of those times was small and the produce of the cow and goat (the poor man's cow) was a very necessary addition to the community's store of food.

Hence the main homestead came to be fixed in the shelter of the lower lands, where some spring crops could be grown and where winter could be passed in comfort. This was the *hendre* or *pentre*, a simple structure of the house-in-loose-order or rambling type, occupied from the approach of winter till the crops were safely in the ground. Towards May occurred the

migration of all or part of the stock-owner's family
to the summer pastures, whereon and grouped in small
hamlets associated with the individual winter villages
were the flimsy structures making the summer dwelling,
the *hafod* or *meifod*. The amount of stock kept in the
earlier time would probably be insufficient to cause
over-stocking, and the use of the pasturage would be
unrestricted.

The hafod was abandoned some time in August, when
there was a migration, not to the hendre, but to the
*cynhacafdy*, for the harvest operations, after which the
family moved to the steading for the winter. The goats
and cattle would give some manure for this agricultural
land.

The journey from the hendre to the hafod might be
short, or of many miles length. It involved all the
baggage and apparatus required for the people and their
dairying activities. The " summer " butter and cheese
produced upon the fresh, open grassland was of excellent
quality, and in course of time came to be of great
importance in the fairs and markets of the thirteenth
century. The extent of the cattle-keeping depended
upon the amount of winter feed in the shape of straw
and hay that the farm could provide, which was not
really very much, so that by the end of the season the
animals were in a pitiable plight, even though, as early
as the fourteenth century, the numbers were considerably
reduced by sales of the best conditioned beasts after
the autumn pasturing upon the stubble and aftermath.

In these early centuries, sheep-keeping in Wales was
of minor importance and not a peasant industry. The
Cistercian monks, however, later introduced some large-
scale sheep-farming, wool, rather than meat, being the
main object of the stock-keeping.

Between the sixteenth and eighteenth centuries the

cattle industry of Wales underwent a great expansion. The Welsh stores or runts were eagerly sought by the English graziers for fattening in the English Midlands and south-eastern counties, and during these same centuries sheep began to appear in large numbers on the Welsh hills though it was not until the end of the seventeenth century that they reached anything approaching the present-day census. The new invaders of the grassland could not supply the milk, butter, and cheese of the cattle whose place they had usurped, and with the introduction of imported food the necessity for the summer migration has disappeared. To-day only a few professional herdsmen accompany the animals to the heights ; the nomadism is an institution of the past.

In course of time the ownership of the summer pastures has changed hands. Originally belonging to the community collectively, as the conception of private property developed, they gradually became part of the general estate of a ground landlord, their use being included in the rent extracted for the farm.

The birth of English Farming is so remote, that the location and scope of its initial periods can only be guessed at by traditions lingering in remote places, deductions based upon generally accepted views concerning other times, and the faint traces upon the country-side which air photography has done so much to discover. It has to be admitted, however, that such evidence is susceptible of diverse interpretations, but though perhaps every selection is open to controversy, it may be wisest to make and abide by some particular choice.

We have to begin with the surface of England as it appeared before the devastating hand of man had destroyed our forests and drained our swamps. Rainfall heavier than in our times fed rivers whose overflow

produced much marsh, and on the sea coast the unchecked tidal encroachments worked to the same effect.
Above the marshes and damp woods of the valleys the
timber line in favoured districts rose beyond the 500-
foot contour ; and open tracts of heath or grassland
furnished the primitive inhabitants with sites for life
and labour upon sands and gravels and limestone and
chalk soils.

These early human groups appear to have placed
their settlements on the bare uplands. We call these
people Neolithic, and ascribe to them a Mediterranean
origin. Their tools and implements, constructed of flint
or bone or horn, were of varied though limited utility,
and often of remarkably fine workmanship. Great
ponds near the summits of the downs supplied them
with water, these reservoirs being filled by rain or
condensation of mist, or the surface drainage from
above, the streams in the chalk districts probably
running at a higher level then than they do to-day.[1]
Sufficient pasture was to hand, and to prevent straying
the sheep and cattle could be impounded within the
great earthwork enclosure at night. Some of these
hill camps included ponds for water, pit dwellings,
flint quarries, terraces for agriculture, ditches, and
multiple walls. A wolf platform (called in Wiltshire
" Shepherds' Steps ") behind which rose sheer the
defending rampart of earth, lessened the danger of
cattle stampeding. The grazing near the encampment,
the cut or plucked grass to provide some winter forage,
the open pasture all the year round, concluded the
pastoral resources of these moorland communities.

[1] Cf. Pitt-Rivers. Some consider the ponds of Celtic workmanship. If so, the natural rain supplied the earlier peoples,
and the making of the ponds may have been necessitated by an
era of decreasing rainfall, which would lower the water table in
the chalk.

In due course this form of life underwent considerable changes caused by the need for more house-room for the growing tribes, or by the enterprise and encouragement of invaders. The Downlands became more systematically distributed among the communities whose terrain ran downhill to the valley. This may be the beginning of the wild grass husbandry. Patches of grain were cultivated with the hoe on the terraced slopes of the hills, changed yearly where the soil was poor, but otherwise more permanent. Some patches of grass, enclosed between low embankments, may have been definitely set aside for hay or grazing areas.

At a still later date a fresh wave of invasion swept the country. The main body consisted of peasants, but peasants having aristocratic and military leaders from a different ancestral home. These invaders possessed leaf-shaped swords and bronze axes. They began to arrive about 1150 B.C., and soon dominated eastern England and Scotland, and pushed on towards Wales and Ireland. Eventually they mastered all England[1] except the mountain country of the south-west. The peasant element came from regions where agriculture was rather highly organized, the leading feature being group cultivation under the ægis of its protecting lord. Their superior implements allowed some deforestation, so that more land was gained for cultivation from the cleared hill-sides and valley bottoms. Riverine territory was cleared for water meadows, thus providing good pasture and hay at the appropriate seasons, and an area of cultivation consisting of three great fields was marked out for each group, to be tilled and enjoyed in common on the plan of the ancient home in Central Europe.

Each original downland village community, enlarged

[1] Following Peake, *The English Village*, p. 85 ff.

and reorganized to some extent by its conquerors, split up into a dozen or so groups, the main part of its population descending to the valley, where new villages sprang up on some suitably dry site not too far from water. Not all the upland villages, however, were broken up, and in the south-western counties some wild grass husbandry was practised under the new conditions, tracts of grass being ploughed and tilled for corn, to relapse into pasture when the soil had become exhausted.

Though the village had now become located in the valley, the cattle, sheep, and goats were still pastured aloft during the summer, the old upland site and its adjacent grazing providing a " common pasturage and a cattle compound " for the stock of the valley community, under the charge of professional herdsmen. The increase in the number of the animals probably led to a further construction of these so-called entrenched hill-forts, many of which may never have been anything else but cattle compounds and a summer home for the main part of the community from May to July, when harvest work necessitated a return of the male population though there was still pasture on the slopes.

Cows formed the most important part of the domestic stock of the Celts, and provided milk, flesh, hides, traction, and coinage. The legal herd of 24 cows was contributed by the various households of the hamlet, each herd being served by one or more bulls.

The enlargement of the grazing grounds " down hill " led to the definite formation of cattle ways, which often ran in duplicate. The animals descended in the morning by the shorter and steeper track, made by repeated treading along the same route. At night they returned by the longer, but easier path. Tally houses placed at the beginning of the ascent and at the entrance to the compound enabled the herdsman in charge to make the necessary count, and ponds constructed on lower ground beyond the camp enabled the animals to be watered both morning and night.

In winter the animals were driven down to the lowland pastures near the homestead, and penned at night in the owner's yard, where there was a supply of hay.

This common herding of the cattle necessitated some kind of a periodic conference among the cattle owners, to decide such matters as time for branding, ownership of calves, payment of herdsmen, etc. A " common " churn was used on the hill pastures, and the collective produce divided among the cattle-owners in accordance with an organized milking test.

At a later date there was a considerable invasion of Belgic lords and their followers, the majority of whom settled in the lands south of the Thames. They probably left the organization of the village community untouched, the original Celtic system of agriculture persisting in its essentials throughout the Roman Interlude.

## CHAPTER VI

## TRANSHUMANCE IN BRITAIN

A N outstanding feature of the mode of life formerly
in operation in the regions just described was the
regularly recurring seasonal migration of the flocks and
herds in search of pasture. Such a seasonal migration
has come to be called " transhumance ", a word derived
from *trans* (across) and *humus* (the ground or soil). The
earliest printed mention of the word transhumance and
its derivatives as generally accepted terms appears in
Villeneuve's *Statistiques* of 1829, where a cause of the
journeying—default of food under the summer wither-
ing of pastures—is plainly stated. The term probably
originated in connection with the migratory flocks of
Spain, whose summer and winter pastures were often
several hundred miles apart. In hilly and mountainous
countries such journeyings are comparatively short, altitude being here responsible for the presence of cool
and luscious summer pastures at no more than a walking distance from the sun-scorched territory of the home
farm. Short wanderings of this description were first
extensively studied in the European Alps, and the
associated life of the stock-owners is known to French-
speaking geographers as *La vie de relations*, which may
be interpreted " the pastoral mountain life ".

These migratory movements may be classified in
various ways, the main differentiation being between
normal and inverse transhumance. The normal variety
has been studied exhaustively in Provence, when from
very remote times the great flock-owners of the plains

of the Lower Rhône have sent their sheep in bands of 6,000 to 40,000 to summer pastures upon the mountains to the east, the transit being " on the hoof " and occupying periods varying from a few days to a month. This migration was necessitated by lack of summer pasturage in the plain, together with the great discomfort of heat, drought, dust-laden winds, and insect pests. It was supervised by " professional " shepherds, the flock-owners remaining in the lowlands.

The high valleys of these mountains just mentioned contained their population of mountain folk, also feeding their stock in summer upon these elevated pastures, whose excellent verdure supported not only the transhumants from the plains, but additional stock far greater in number than the mountain folk could support in winter. They thus in autumn entrusted their flocks in full or in part to the shepherds of the " great transhumance ", who took them with their own charges to the Rhône plain, where, with the local stock, they were spread out on the fields of the cultivator, devouring his stubble or grass, and providing animal manure for soil enrichment. In the spring these flocks were returned to their owners on the heights. This downward exile is distinguished as " inverse transhumance ". There is still a considerable survival of both the normal and inverse transhumance in south-eastern France and in other parts of Europe.

The pastoral mountain life is obviously also a form of transhumance. As the journeyings connected with it are short, it may be distinguished as the " lesser transhumance ". The practical details of the migration differ in different localities, but a very usual variety is the " great mountain exploitation " of the Savoie Alps. In this case the stock-owners dwell in the mountain valley, and the cattle of one or more villages or hamlets are amalgamated into a single herd and sent for the summer " to the mountain " or local Alpine pastures, under the supervision of a little band of professional herdsmen. The pastures are under communal ownership, and the cattle pasture " in common ", though different pastures are assigned to the cattle being reared only for meat, and to the cows. With regard to the latter, the daily milk of the herd is amalgamated and converted into large cheeses which are subsequently sold, the price received being divided among the cow-owners in proportion to the number of cows possessed and the tested value of each cow's milk. In the autumn the cows return home, and after pasturing in the open upon the various aftermaths of the summer harvests, are finally " enclosed " and stall-fed through the winter months. A variation of this system occurs where spring and autumn pasture can be obtained at some intermediate level (e.g. the Swiss Mayen) between the Alpine pasture and the valley village. The cows may spend these seasons at these levels under the supervision of their owners, all or part of the family migrating with them and inhabiting simple dwellings at these heights, the cows providing much of the family food in terms of milk and cheese. Where the altitude is not too great and the climate propitious, the family, in all or in part, may spend the complete summer with their stock on the high pastures. In this case again the cattle are under the family supervision, and the cheeses produced are small, and intended for the family use. This is the " little mountain exploitation ". In winter the village milk is amalgamated in a factory (*fruitière*) where large cheeses are made for sale and export. Migrations involving a part or all of the *family* are known as " seasonal nomadism ". [1]

[1] For detailed accounts of transhumance and pastoral nomadism in Southern Europe, see my *Water and Grass*.

The above brief reference to the very extensive transhumance still existing in Europe has carried us far from
Britain, but this straying has not been without design.
Transhumance, though "typically" an attribute of
regions of summer drought, has been and is widely prevalent in our own country, where it shows nearly all the
varieties existing elsewhere.

For, when the matter is probed to its roots, the
migration is seen to be based on the primal necessity for
food, whatever the causes whereby shortage is brought
about in the home region. In Domesday times the
submergence of the Marshes of Kent and Essex and
the Norfolk Fens drove the flocks that fed upon them
in summer to seek a winter refuge upon neighbouring
uplands, a transhumance surviving in part where the
winter climate renders these now-drained marshes too
bleak for young sheep.

Transhumance is still a feature of Bodmin Moor and
Dartmoor. Cattle and sheep are depastured on these
heights from May until October. The "forest" of Dartmoor, comprising some 30,000 acres, belongs to the
Duchy of Cornwall. From ancient times the tenant
moormen have enjoyed pastoral rights in this "forest"
by virtue of their farm holding. A nominal rent is
charged for this use and low stone walls mark off a
separate piece of the moor for each of the twenty-one
moorland parishes. The moormen also appear to enclose
at need additional land for providing winter forage.
Their hired labourers enjoy grazing privileges in the
zone of their employer's parish, but not right of enclosure. Parishes further away possess commonage
rights for small payment, and even "foreigners" from
far beyond the region send hither their animals in
summer on a "great transhumance". This pasture is
in much request in dry seasons; Galloway cattle are

found here, though Cornwall and Devon naturally supply the majority of the transhumants. The migration, primarily caused by shortage of pasture in the home region, results in part from the fact that sheep and cattle summering on Dartmoor thrive better on their return home. The moormen supervise this alien pasturing, which is paid for at the rate of 5s. per head of cattle and 25s. per score of sheep. The prices are higher in the case of the *newtakes*, or better grazings.

Cultivation in this district is dominated by the needs of the stock; forage roots, clover, rotation grasses, and dredge corn (a mixture of oats and barley) being the chief. On certain parts of the moorland rim the village stock feeds after August on the aftermath of grass in the fields irrespective of ownership.

Formerly there was an immense tract of unenclosed hill and moor, stretching from the neighbourhood of Wells almost to the Bristol Channel, and making part of the great Forest of Mendip. The immense flocks of this region ranged from moor to hill and hill to moor, as the season required. [1]

Our northern islands are still the scene of long-standing practices. In Lewis (Outer Hebrides), on the approach of summer the young members of the family go up with their stock to their turf dwellings or " airidhs " in the hill pastures; dairying is the summer activity. This migration is similar to that of the summer seasonal nomadism from the Fiord villages of Norway to the sæter, and is still to be found in the Western Isles of Scotland and among the Scottish Highlands.

It would be a delightful exercise to sort out and match the various instances of transhumance in Britain with their European analogues. The normal and inverse Provençal Transhumance is represented by the Great

[1] W. Youatt, *The Sheep*, 1837, p. 256.

Transhumance of Dartmoor and the Lake District. This latter, in addition, has some resemblance to the migratory pastoral industry of the Spanish " Mesta of the Shepherds " (1272–1836), which is said to owe its name to the Spanish word *mesta*, or meeting, and as such applied to the periodic assembling of the sheep-owners. This word mesta has also been derived from the word *mestenos* (a stray), some of the objects of the meeting being to deal with the yearly engagements of the shepherds and the return of the stray sheep to their owners. These functions are fulfilled at the " Shepherds' Meet " mentioned in connection with the Herdwicks of the Lake District. We cannot have anything to parallel the long journeys of the Mesta flocks, but from Brecon, Radnor, and the Black Mountains of Carmarthenshire sheep still travel 30 or 40 miles to the Cardiganshire coast and from 40 to 75 miles from North Cardiganshire to the neighbourhood of Portmadoc, Criccieth, and the Vale of Clwyd. Young sheep may be on the road from one to three days, though the long-distance journeys in Wales, as in modern Provence, are generally done by rail.[1] Each October thousands of sheep migrate to the lowlands to return with their lambs in March.

The enormous sheep walks of the Mesta were paralleled in early times by the three great sheep walks of Wales, one of which occupied the whole of Anglesey and harboured 120,000 sheep. The flock-master of this " walk " employed a chief shepherd under whom worked 300 assistants and followers. A second sheep run, extending from the Menai Straits to the River Severn and from Cardigan Bay to the Dee Estuary, included the rest of North Wales. The remaining pastures of the country made up the third great sheep walk.

The pastoral mountain life with its upland summer

[1] *Geography Teacher*, No. 55, Vol. X, p. 106, Aug. 1919.

grazing grounds and winter residence in the mountain villages is still and has been a feature of our pastoral industry from very early times.   Just as in the Southern French Alps, the dales of our Pennine Uplands give winter pasture or stall-feeding, the summer being spent aloft and in the open.   Similar movements occur in East Anglia, where large numbers of cattle find summer pastures in the sandy region with winter stall-feeding at the farms.   Examples have also been given of a seasonal nomadism in Britain of the kind so much associated with the simple and complex migrations of the pastoral mountains of the French and Italian Alps.

In Britain, as abroad, the migratory pastoral industry has its problems of the " dead " season.   In Lewis, as in Switzerland, the women spin thread for some branch of the textile industry ;  the homespun Harris tweed may be compared justly with the Swiss lace-making. In the European Alps and the Central Plateau of France it is very customary for some members of the pastoral families to seek employment outside the home region, their pastoral duties being reduced or taken over by others.   While the young people of Lewis are with the domestic stock at the shieling, the mother is " following the fish " on land as a " Scotch lassie ", and the father and older sons have hired themselves to some fishing-smack owner.

## CHAPTER VII

## BEGINNINGS IN LOWER BRITAIN

THE organization of the valley villages of our Southern Scarplands, outlined in Chapter V, has also been ascribed to the Saxons. Peake points out that these latter invaders came from a land where a one-field system of agriculture was in force, and that on settling in Britain they probably continued the practice they found in working order.[1]

The 3-field system which played so large a part in the agriculture of mediæval times is known to us as the open-field system, because the tilled area was not bounded by any permanent fences or hedges. Whether initiated in Britain before or after the Roman occupation, it had a very long life, lasting into the seventeenth and eighteenth centuries though other systems had firmly established themselves before its disappearance. This long life makes it difficult to describe in general terms since something was added and something was taken from it in each successive century.[2] All that can be attempted here is a description of the agricultural and pastoral workings of a feudal village generalized to cover the Saxon, Norman, Plantagenet, and later period. The term " manor village " is, of course, a Norman introduction after 1066, but it is only a new name for an older situation. The system was especially developed in south and south-eastern England.

[1] Peake, *op. cit.*, p. 101.
[2] A century by century description is given in M. E. Seebohm's *The Evolution of the English Farm*, 1927.

The manor village consisted mainly of a group of people some of whom were free, some " unfree ", and the lord of the manor, who held his land at a more or less direct vassalage from the king. A number of manors, however, were held by the titular heads of the great ecclesiastical houses. The manor lands were worked in three unequal sections, namely, the lord's demesne, the common fields, and the common pastures. The demesne was the smallest section, a compact block worked to the profit of its individual owner, and wherein was situated the manor house. The largest section consisted of the cultivable fields, shared out among the members of the village group and the lord of the manor, and cultivated " in common " for their personal benefit. The village lay amid these tillage fields, and where the nature of the land permitted, there was some grassland along the river course, part providing grazing for cows, part grazing for bullocks, and the rest meadows for hay. The third section of the estate included the common pasture lands, fringed by woodland and the uncultivated moors, heaths, scrublands, marshes, etc., that isolated each manor village from its neighbours. Right of use in this pasture, woodland, and waste belonged to the lord of the manor as ground landlord, to the villagers by virtue of their share in the arable land, and to the dwellers in certain cottages belonging to the estate.[1] All the cultivation was done by the men-folk of the villages, who worked both on their own behalf, and in corvée for their lord, by which service, together with some payment in kind, the rental dues for house and farm holding were settled. The object of the manor

[1] In the earlier centuries the lord had a greater share in the common cultivation, but no private estate. By the middle of the fourteenth century the enclosed demesne for the lord's benefit was very general. Originally the lord merely guarded or protected the waste ; later he assumed its ownership.

F

farming was to meet the entire needs of the community in food and clothing.  The common pasture provided grazing for the young stock ; where this pasture was " stinted " its use was strictly in accordance with the amount of arable holding of the villagers, the agistment of ex-local cattle and sheep being forbidden.  But the lord often made encroachments on the use of these commons for his personal benefit, or permitted villagers or even outsiders to place extra stock on the commons providing a suitable payment was made to himself.  Some commons were unstinted and consequently so heavily stocked that the animals pasturing upon them were reduced to skin and bone.  Even in good seasons the commons gave barely sufficient grass to satisfy the minimum needs, and in bad seasons the mortality among the stock was high.  Sometimes simple grasslands, these commons were more often mere patches of grass amid a general woodland of oak, ash, and hazel, with much undergrowth and thorn.  The untilled waste and woodland fringing the common pasture provided heath for litter, bedding, and thatching ; turf and furze for fuel ; material for building, timber, fences, carts, ploughs, hurdles, and agricultural implements, together with winter browse, this last being a very valuable addition to the winter food resources.  Acorns and beech mast (pannage) gave pasturage for the swine which were kept in large numbers where woodland predominated.  On well-watered and reedy pastures cattle were supreme, but where there was much open pasture, as on the Downs, sheep were reared very extensively on account of the value of their wool.

In the lowest part of the manor lands, if possible along a stream, lay the water meadows, the *ings, carrs, leazes* of the various regions.  From July to February or later this land was used as open common pasturage,

but in early spring it was cut up into strips and allotted
to the villagers in proportion to their arable holding.
The same individual might or might not hold a given
strip two years running. When the hay grass began to
grow the strips were fenced off, and about July the
bailiff and tenants agreed upon the date of mowing.
On the appointed morning all the villagers turned out for
the haymaking. On Lammas Day the hayward removed the hurdles, and each tenant sent in his own
cattle.

The paramount aim of the arable cultivation was to
raise corn and barley for bread and beer, though peas
and beans were also largely grown. The arable land
was worked in three great fields to which such names
as Northfield, Eastfield, etc., were given. In any one
year two of these fields were under cultivation, the third
resting, or lying fallow, but not as a true bare fallow,
since weeds were allowed to spring up as they afforded
some sustenance to the village livestock. The fallow
was manured by folding sheep upon it, and so prepared for the succeeding crop of wheat. The method of
cultivation can be expressed thus :

|  | Field A. | Field B. | Field C. |
|---|---|---|---|
| 1st year . | Wheat or Rye | Barley or Oats | Fallow |
| 2nd year . | Barley or Oats | Fallow | Wheat or Rye |
| 3rd year . | Fallow | Wheat or Rye | Barley or Oats |

MANOR VILLAGE. ANCIENT 3-COURSE ROTATION

The barley field might be sown with beans, peas, or
oats ; both the wheat and rye were sown in autumn,
the barley in spring. The yield of wheat and rye was
about 10 bushels per acre ; barley yielded a little more
and oats a little less. Originally the rotation consisted

of two corn crops followed by a fallow. The production provided straw for winter forage.

The practical details of the co-operative farming were somewhat as follows. In Anglo-Saxon times different grades of peasantry enjoyed special privileges and fulfilled special functions. The gebur, the most free and the direct representative of the original peasant, had 30 acres in the cornfield, the cottier about five. Other peasants were bee-keepers, oxherds, cowherds, shepherds, goatherds, swineherds, and the like. By ploughing extra land for the lord, the wealthy gebur was able to put on the common pasture a number of cattle he possessed in excess of his status. Otherwise each partner—freeman or bondman of the village association —cultivated a share of the arable land in proportion to services in labour or kind rendered or owed to the lord of the manor. This lord also possessed a share as the ground landlord, and the parson a share by virtue of his office. Each year the cultivable land was divided up into acre or half-acre strips, separated from each other by a balk of turf, and the strips were assigned among the co-partners in allotments so arranged that no one individual had all the strips of his allotment in a compact block, nor any of the same pieces of ground two years running. By this means no one man had the poorer soil twice in succession, while the crops cultivated followed the strict rotation. From seed-time to harvest the arable was surrounded by moveable fences in order to keep out the cattle ; but when the harvesting was over the fences were removed, and the community domestic stock fed " promiscuously " in the stubble, thus providing some manuring for the next crop.

The animal manure was regarded as so essential that often the villagers were compelled to fold their sheep on the lord's holding, and, less generally, their cattle. This was the service of " fold-soke ".

The majority of the sheep of the open-field farming were short-wools ; small, active, hardy, they could eke out existence on the most meagre fare and travel long distances without undue fatigue.  Their customary food was the poor pasturage of the commons, chases, forest, etc., eaten over by the communal flocks " in common ", and during the summer.  The weeds and aftergrowths upon the fallows, the stubble, and the aftermaths also provided some sustenance.  In general the winter food was specially prepared peas' haulms, oat straw, etc., and the lopping from certain trees (including mistletoe and ivy) whose leaves and tenderer twigs were gathered in autumn and dried for this purpose.

Each morning during summer the village shepherd, assisted by his dog, drove his sheep to the pastures, keeping a watch upon them all day to see they came to no harm.  Twice a day (three times a day in the month of May) the ewes were led to the sheds to be milked, there being some demand for ewes'-milk butter and cheese.  At night the sheep returned home, and were folded on the fallow in a " common fold ", which was moved at intervals in such a way that the field should be manured more or less evenly.  The shepherd slept in a moveable hut near his charges.  The sheep were washed and sheared after midsummer, the shearing of the lord's flock being part of service owed by his tenantry. The wool and wool fells were an important source of the manor income.  Between Whitsuntide and Easter the flocks received a special inspection, when the old or feeble sheep or crones whose teeth were too worn for them to be able to feed any longer on the pastures were given a better food, so that they could be fattened for sale about St. John's Day, to be finished off for

the Michaelmas slaughter and salting for winter consumption.   In the general flock ewe-milking ceased in
autumn, in order that the sheep might be in as good a
condition as possible to meet the hardships of winter.

Lambing was often timed to take place about Candlemas (February 2nd), a date making it possible for the
lambs to be fattened for the Helenmas sale (May 3rd).
Where there were special pastures lambing might be
later.   In the open hill country ewes and lambs occupied
low-lying pastures from Lady Day till September, when
they were folded mainly on rye land.   The sheep were
housed from Martinmas to Easter, but allowed to lie
out in the fold when the weather was propitious.   When
the fold was placed on cultivated land, each sheep-owner
had to find his own fold and fodder for his flock.   From
Martinmas to Easter the unfree villagers lay in turn
at night in the lord's sheep folds or sheds near the manor
to guard against thieves.

The shepherd of the manor village was looked upon
as a cheerful man, whose prowess with horn and bag-
pipe contributed greatly to the village merriment.   A
long cloak and a curved staff were his badges of office.
Besides his other duties, he was in charge of the lambing, branded the sheep annually, milked the ewes, and
kept the sheep-cote or permanent fold well thatched and
in good repair.   Summer and winter, he and his dog
slept near the sheep.   The shepherd was, of course, one
of the unfree.   His payment was partly in kind and
partly in opportunities ;  each year he received one lamb
of the year's increase, a bell-wether's fleece, the milk of
his flock for seven consecutive nights after the equinox,
and a bowl of whey each night during summer.   From
Christmas to the Epiphany, he might fold his flocks on
his own land ;  his sheep fed in with the common flock.

During Norman times the supervision became more

differentiated, and there grew up a keeper of the wethers (or muttons), a keeper of the ewes, and sometimes a keeper of the lambs.

The general management of the sheep naturally varied with the geographical and climatic circumstances. In the north of England, where the manorial system was less strong, the sheep generally remained on the open hills all the year round. They were collected for shearing and branding, and at harvest time they were driven into large folds and sorted out for ownership, after which many were killed and salted for winter. Sheep houses, situated in the home yard or by a stack-yard, where hay and other crops were stored, were used only in the summer, when the milk was required at home. Cheese and clotted cream were important products.

In the case of cattle, stock, milk, skins, manure, and field service were the objectives of the industry. Only the upper classes ate meat from cattle reared solely as beef cattle.

In summer the animals lived an outdoor life. Each morning the herdsman passed through the village blowing his horn, at which signal the cattle of the different owners not required for field service went out to join the swelling herd, which made its way to the pastures by cattle routes or drift ways fenced with hurdles or stakes to prevent straying. The herdsman spent the whole day with the cattle and at night brought them back to the village, where each animal was returned to its own shelter as the diminishing herd went by.

The oxen employed at field labour, after being " unjobbed ", were led off to pasture upon fallow, and looked after by the oxherd, who also slept in their stable to prevent theft. There was generally some special grazing for the cattle near the village, but they also pastured on the stubble and in the meadows after the corn and

hay harvests.  At the end of June, draught cows and
worn-out oxen were fed up in preparation° for slaughter,
and at the end of August old cows ceased to be milked
with the same object.  When ready the " fat " animals
were sold or killed at home and salted for home consumption.  Martinmas was the great date for killing
stock not to be wintered.  Cows kept under cover in
cold weather were allowed out once a day for exercise
and drink.  From St. Luke's Day to April the draught
oxen were kept in stall.  All the cattle received a winter
food of various sorts of straw and hay.  By January,
most of this fodder was eaten, and the food now consisted of " browse ", or cut branches of suitable trees and
shrubs.  In May the grassland of sheltered closes received the calves.

The cowherd drove his herd out to pasture each day,
and saw they were well housed at night and provided
with litter or fern.  He slept with them to ensure their
safety.  He also milked them, but the milk was worked
up by the dairy women.  Like the ewes, the cows
were milked three times a day during the " month of
the three milkings " (May).  After 1066, except where
there was a good supply of forage, cows were only
milked between May and Michaelmas.  Cheese not required for the lord's table was made of skim milk.
The " summer " butter was sold or salted and preserved
in pots and tubs for winter.  The buttermilk was drunk
as such, or curded and used either for fattening pigs, or
eaten with wine or ale.  Whey, often called " whig ", was
a good summer drink.  The " winter " milk was very
small in quantity ; it was usually sold, or calves were
timed to fall before Christmas.

The herdsman, like the shepherd, received his pay
partly in kind and partly in opportunities.  The cowherd was allowed the milk of an old cow for seven days

after calving (whence he could obtain cheese) and the
" beastings " of a young cow for 14 days.  The oxherd
could pasture two or more oxen and a cow with his
lord's herd, and was given his shoes, gloves, and keep.

Though at no time prevalent over the whole of England, and considerably modified from the fourteenth
century and onward, the manor system of village life
existed right down into the modern period.  At the
beginning of the eighteenth century, more than half of
the arable land of England was still being cultivated on
this plan.

## CHAPTER VIII

## THE MOVEMENT TOWARDS PASTURAGE

THE highly systematized method of farming just considered, was at no time in operation over the whole country. Even in the Anglo-Saxon period there were variations in the method of holding and cultivating the land, though where the manor village had been established there was no serious breach in the system until the twelfth century. But it was by no means unusual for the lord of the manor to secure extra meadow and arable land for his own use, and when it could be done with safety the villagers took to enclosing pieces of the waste and farming it for individual benefit, placating the ground landlord for this unjustifiable encroachment by extra service. Sometimes the better off villagers made private arrangements with each other by which they exchanged or rearranged their arable strips for permanent enclosure, whereby they gained more land for cultivation by the abolition of the balks, and having no one but themselves to please, were able to grow a greater variety of crops. On the other hand, though the ideal of the manor system was to promote an equitable enjoyment of the land based on the villager's status, in practice, the poorer the villager the less his proportional benefit ; thus a commoner possessing larger pasture rights could reserve his grass till the last possible moment by using the common, and later, when the feudal system was weakening, disputes settled in the law courts were generally given in favour of the richer man. Where pastures were unstinted, stock-dealers

with capital frequently hired land at double rentage on
the edge of the common, and so claimed grazing rights,
and over-stocked from their own supply or by agisting
the stock of strangers.

In course of time there came into existence enclosure
not for arable, but for pastoral purposes.  After the
Black Death a large trade in skins and leather developed,
and land was enclosed for additional cattle pasture
necessitated by this trade.  But far more serious was
the enclosing for sheep-rearing.  The growing demand
for our wool both at home and abroad made large-scale
sheep farming very profitable.  The keeping quality of
wool was a great asset in this age of bad roads, since it
was more easily and cheaply transported on the pack-
mule, whereas grain required a wheeled vehicle.  The
great landlords were the earliest of these commercial
sheep farmers, and they established the new farming
by enclosing large tracts of common or grassland.  This
method of enclosure made the supervision of the sheep
better and cheaper, and prevented disputes as to the
position of the boundaries of the farms.  After the
Black Death (c. 1349) the enclosure movement grew
rapidly.  One result of the enormous depopulation was
that numerous holdings in the villages were left without
owners or heirs, and were thus returned to the manor
ownership pending disposal to a new holder.  There was
no surplus of villagers to cultivate them, while freemen
of the towns, who might have taken them up, refused
to do so except at a much higher payment than the
bondmen had received.  The change from arable to
grass seemed a way out of the difficulty, pasturage
requiring much less hand labour than agriculture.

The results of the battle of Bosworth Field (1485) gave
another impetus towards pasturage.  The lavish hospitality of the feudal lords was not emulated by the

new landlords, who, keeping smaller houses, needed less agricultural produce to sustain them, and again much arable passed into pasture.  One consequence of this change was the creation of excessive unemployment, the ranks of the landless again increasing, though work was to be found for many in the growing woollen and other industries of the Tudor period.

The dissolution of the monasteries, about 1536, worked in the same sense, for the titular heads of the ecclesiastical houses were also in the position of lords of manors. The new owners of the monastic lands having no feudal tie with the local peasantry, enclosed for pasture what had been open-field territory, without any regard for the needs of the villagers.  At the same time agriculture gained something from the changed circumstances.  The break with tradition enabled the landlords to experiment with a view to improving both livestock and crops, and it was naturally easier for the more substantial freemen and villeins to buy up, exchange, and consolidate their own holdings.  These freemen and villeins became the yeomen or occupying owners of farms quite outside manorial jurisdiction and so were able to farm in accordance with their personal ideas.  Where the ancient system still remained, in many regions a certain slackness crept into its operations, fallows being omitted and dung, once devoted entirely to manurial purposes, being dried and used for fuel ;  such breaches in the old system furthered soil depreciation at a time when arable cultivation outside the system was improving.

Towards the end of the fifteenth and onward into the sixteenth century outbreaks of murrain destroyed large numbers of sheep and cattle, the open-field farmer suffering most.  As a result, much common right became valueless, and the associated arable holding a burden rather than a benefit.  Many open-field farmers

surrendered their holdings, and not being able to obtain
day labour at the declining agricultural cultivation, went
to the towns, there to support themselves as industrial
labourers, or to add to the ever-increasing host of the
unemployed.

During the years 1485 to 1560 enclosure for pastoral
exploitation was particularly active. When the enclosing affected village property peasants were evicted
wholesale, villages were destroyed, and the distress
through unemployment reached unprecedented heights.
There were not wanting denunciations of the new
system. Philosophers such as Bacon, agriculturists
such as Fitzherbert, philanthropists such as Sir Thomas
More, preachers such as Latimer, and a host of lesser
lights such as the scribblers of satires and street ballads,
inveighed loudly but ineffectually against it. Equally
ineffective was parliamentary opposition, too many of
the nobility and richer classes being involved in this
profitable enterprise. Moreover, it must be recognized
that in many respects the manor system had really out-
grown its usefulness, while long cultivation had so
impoverished much of the soil that a return to pasture
was needed to restore it to vigour. At the same time
during these difficult years there was much reclaiming
of forest and true waste, thus giving to agriculture a
soil whose fertility had not been exhausted, and whereby
the corn crop of the country was probably maintained.

In spite of rural distress the nation as a whole derived
much benefit from the new large-scale sheep farming.
The wool tax paid for the foreign wars of Henry VIII,
and by the time of Queen Elizabeth, the commercial
prosperity of the country depended on the wool trade.
Emulating the practice of the monks, those former large-
scale sheep owners, the grateful wool merchants at
their own expense caused to be constructed beautiful

churches and fine buildings, as well as very necessary roads.

The desire to produce fleeces of good selling value naturally led to better management of the stock. The practice of milking ewes began to decline, for among English flock-masters, as among the Shepherds of the Spanish Mesta, milking was considered to affect adversely the fineness of the fleece. Before lambing time the " enclosed " sheep, were brought into good, well-sheltered pastures near the farm-house ; the sheep were given special pastures and were folded on rye in May. In winter these favoured sheep had a meal made of peas and barley ground together, or dried peas and acorns, and green or dry " 3-leaved grass ". The commercial sheep farmer owned flocks varying from 5,000 to 24,000 head, the most popular breeds being the small, black-faced breeds of Hereford, Worcester and Shropshire. Cotswold wool was heavier, but longer and coarse ; much of the Welsh wool also was coarse and even kempy (hairy), so that these sheep were considered inferior to all others and to be " praised only in the dish " on account of the good mutton flavour.

Towards the latter end of the Tudor period cattle began to come into their own ; under better feeding and management draught oxen were better proportioned and meat cattle of finer flesh. The tall, long-legged Lincoln cattle were preferred for labour and draught, and the longhorns of Lancashire, Yorkshire, Derbyshire, and Staffordshire became reputed for goodness of meat. A true dairy industry began to make its appearance. During the earlier part of the 17th century, the dairy industry extended to the valleys of the west and south-west, and from the middle of this century heavy milking cows were imported from the Low Countries, thus introducing continental blood.

British livestock, with all their faults, were more than holding their own in foreign competition, and even arousing considerable enthusiasm at home. " Where are oxen more large of bone," wrote William Harrison about 1580, " kine more commodious for the pail, sheep more profitable for wool, . . . than here with us in England ? " [1]

[1] *Description of Britain.*

## CHAPTER IX

## THE PASTORAL REVOLUTION—1. FOOD AND FORAGE

JUDGED by modern standards, the grain grown by British farmers down to the eighteenth century was of very poor quality. Only the straw was fed to the domestic livestock and made the major part of the winter feed, rough and meadow pasture, and hay, with some little assistance from browse, peas' haulms, and the like, completing the annual forage supply. It was not possible to feed much domestic livestock through the winter, and stock not required to keep up the herd or flock, or to meet special needs such as milking, was slaughtered before winter to be consumed as fresh meat, or was salted or smoked for use later in the season.

Although thus reduced in numbers, their winter food was all too scanty, and the sheep and cattle spent that season in an enfeebling state of semi-starvation so that even with the better summer conditions a cow seldom gave more than 300 gallons of milk a year and the average weight of a sheep's fleece was about one pound. The hay was fed to the young stock as far as it would go, working bullocks and heavy milking cows getting some with their straw in times of plenty, and an occasional sheaf of unthreshed oats. As soon as possible the young stock were put upon the strict straw diet and kept on it until they were sufficiently old to be useful.

The open-field system defied all attempts at agricultural improvement. It was sufficient for one man to stand out against the introduction of new crops or methods for the suggested improvement to fall through. Though each co-partner had his fair share of field and fallow, the annual rearrangement of strips discouraged him from personally improving his allotment of any given year, since he was debarred from enjoying this benefit the following year. The custom of feeding the cattle in autumn upon the stubble might enrich the fields with manure, but prevented the growing of catch crops which would have been a great stand-by for increasing the winter forage. Finally, though flocks and herds of different villages using the same or contiguous commons kept mainly to their own quarters, undesirable promiscuous matings, whether between different breeds or members of the same village stock, were bound to take place, to the detriment of the standard of breed, and to the spreading of sheep and cattle diseases.

However, the breaches in the manorial system referred to in the previous chapter were resulting in some improvement to agriculture. The growth of towns and industries promoted the need for greater food production, and in Stuart times much poor, self-sown pasture, which had arisen through the decline of arable cultivation after the Black Death, was taken back for agriculture, enriched through rest and the droppings of the grazing animals. The interest in an increased agricultural output now resulted in local reclamations of various wastes, and culminated in the great reclamation of the English Fen District, thus adding to the agricultural lands territory so far untouched by the plough.

During this early period of agricultural betterment, the sad condition of British flocks and herds attracted the attention of both literature and the law. As a result of this publicity and the good sense of the large-scale

G

sheep farmers, increased care was given to manuring, and between 1628 and 1636 patents were taken out for reclamation enterprises, new manures, and better ploughs. Laws were issued against " ploughing by the tail " and " plucking the wool off the living sheep ", a practice still in force, however, in the Shetland Islands. The outbreak of the Civil War interfered considerably with agricultural experiments, though one might note that the great war horse, not proving invulnerable to the attack by gunpowder, became a field animal, thereby greatly relieving the ox as a beast of burden. It has been said that at the Restoration the chief need of English farming was the leadership of practical men, endowed with " leisure, capital, initiative and courage ". But another century was to elapse before such leaders were found.

Before and after the Restoration agricultural literature was becoming increasingly tinged with accounts of the livestock and associated industries in the Low Countries. Sir Richard Weston, for example, returning thence, described how turnips, red clover, sainfoin, lucerne, rape and flax grew there in rotation systems superior to those of Great Britain. He laid stress upon the fact that clover, cut twice or thrice a season, was fed to cows in summer, while turnips, oil press refuse, brewers' grains, were fed to stock in winter as produced and at hand, or stored in pits (ensilage) and given later. It is true that by the middle of the seventeenth century most of these foods for livestock had been tried in England, but with little success, the open-field farmers not liking " new notions ", and the " crop upon crop " farmer, with his private piece of land, did not possess the skill to make such farming a success. This was the more unfortunate as the " crop upon crop " method is very exhausting to the soil, while clover and other legumes, with their nitrogen-fixing bacteria, not only supply a winter food for stock, but enrich the soil in which they grow.

The first remarkable advance in scientific farming occurred about the middle of the eighteenth century. The open-field farmer was wont to fling his seed broadcast, but Jethro Tull discovered that crops grew better if the soil was stirred during their growth, a stirring only possible where seeds were planted in rows. This discovery led him to invent a drill-sowing machine, and a horse hoe to stir up the soil. As in the case of most reformers, his work was not appreciated during his lifetime, and his method did not become of general use until after his death.

Contemporaneous with Tull was Charles, second Viscount Townshend (1674–1738), affectionately known as "Turnip Townshend" on account of his farming slogan. After successfully trying Tull's method on the usual crops of the farm economy of the day, he experimented with it on the new crop, turnip, which when sown broadcast was too small to be pulled and carted, but became of sufficient size when sown in drills and thinned out. Such turnips could be carted to cattle sheds and together with hay or straw gave a better winter feed than had so far been known. Townshend's farming experiments, which included heavy marling, were carried out upon the sandy soils of Norfolk, hence their success was very striking. Other Norfolk farmers followed his example, and between them they devised the famous 4-course Norfolk Rotation, wheat, turnips, barley (or some other summer corn), red clover. This rotation, later to become traditional, at first found slow favour, even in Norfolk, and still less outside the county, farmers and landowners in general classing turnips with *rats* as "Hanoverian innovations". However, by the end of the eighteenth century the new rotation was fairly established in Norfolk and, with slight variations necessitated in some districts by the climate and soil, had been introduced to most parts of Britain.

The next great farming experimentalist was Coke of Holkham (1754–1842), later first Lord Leicester. His estates lay among the " good sands " of northern and north-western Norfolk, then an open district where " two rabbits fought for a blade of grass ". At the time of his accession to these estates, Coke had no particular agricultural bent, and his land was so infertile that his tenants refused to continue paying 5s. an acre for it. Being an ardent Whig at a time when the Tory party was in power, he was debarred by his politics from court life or a political career. He therefore devoted himself to farming, dealing personally with as much of his own land as he could, and obtaining good tenants for the rest by giving them good houses and farm buildings. Working along the lines advocated by Townshend, he increased and perfected his forage resources, and improved the Norfolk stock by the introduction of Devonshire cattle and Southdown sheep. His farming ultimately attained a success which brought both to himself and his county a more than local fame. To him we owe the use of artificial foods such as oil-cake, which, with roots, provided the good stall-feeding which came to be extensively practised. He made his personal farming experiments an education for his tenants, and visitors from far and near came to hear him expound his methods. The great Holkham Sheep-shearing was a rendezvous for practical and theoretical agriculturists, pastoral farmers, and breeders of livestock, who talked to each other about their own methods and received advice upon their own difficulties.

At Woburn Abbey the Duke of Bedford carried

on similar experimental farming and held similar
meetings.

This century of agricultural progress in Norfolk, a
country of rich pastures reclaimed from coastal marshes
and adjacent to arable farms and uplands, increased
enormously its resources of forage for additional summer
and winter feed.  A consequence was an unprecedented
influx of store beasts for the Norfolk farmers to fatten
by stall-feeding during the winter for the London market.
An interesting feature of this new farming is the example
it affords of a species of pastoral momentum : the
visitors gave the farmers large quantities of manure,
whereby more land was fertilized, producing more
wheat, which production necessitated large quantities
of subsidiary rotation crops and grasses, whereby an
increased number of stock could be fattened, the cycle
of increase then beginning again.  By the end of the
eighteenth century Norfolk had become an important
factor in the national supply of grain and meat.  Of
the annual 20,000 bullocks fattened in Norfolk 25 per
cent were entirely home fed, and 75 per cent came from
Scotland and Ireland, while the annual deportation of
sheep reached 30,000.

The immediate result of the new agricultural method
was to safeguard the older stock in winter from losing
condition, and to permit the younger to live through
that season without being seriously stunted in growth.
Late calving cows, formerly dry by early autumn, could
now give an increased yield at each milking and be
milked for a longer period, while stock which would
once have been killed and salted about Michaelmas
could now tide over the winter season and be fattened
the following summer, when the joints of meat were
larger than if the animal had been killed the previous
year.  The later introduction of mangolds and swedes

(1783) as a food for farm stock provided a supplementary ration of similar utility.

While these excellent agricultural improvements were in progress, the open-field farming was receiving a blow from which it has never recovered.

Certain breaches in the manor system have already been touched upon ; we have now to consider the effects of a second great enclosure movement, the main object of which was to increase agricultural output. The causes of the enclosure acts of the eighteenth and nineteenth centuries are outside our subject, but we may notice that the rise in the price of corn and consequent increase of rental value, the greater supply of food needed for the growing industrial population, and the improved methods of agriculture all pointed to the necessity for the abolition of the open-field system, which rarely rose above the level of bare subsistence farming. At the outset the peasant was intended to exchange his shifting strip holding for a compact little holding in permanence, retaining his rights in the communal pasture, woodland, and waste, according to the extent of his arable holding. The abolition of the now unnecessary balks between the strips would add a considerable quota to the tillage area. Unfortunately, the expenses of fencing his new estate, the increasing cost of living, the lack of experience in personal responsibility after generations of communal responsibility, made it very difficult for the English peasant to meet the new situation. Rather than take up his new holding under such expensive and novel conditions, he sold his land to the landlord, often at a low figure, the sale being forced, and with this sale went also his other communal rights. Even where the peasant held out for some time, his ultimate disaster was merely deferred, since the new holding rarely satisfied the needs of his household and farm stock.  The domestic industries that once so greatly had helped the family budget were failing before the increasing factory output.  The cottar was in a still worse plight, for, possessing no arable holding, he lost automatically his woodland and pasture rights, and was obliged either to become a labourer in a community which was finding it increasingly difficult to pay wages, or to receive the small dole meted out to the unemployed, or to seek work in the towns.

The tenant farmers, having no traditional right to the soil, were often evicted with a compensation quite inadequate to the continued needs of a family now out of work.  The well-to-do peasants, however, managed to weather the storm.  With the capital derived from the sale of their holding and acquisitions they bought large farms, which were generally prosperous, especially in the neighbourhood of large towns wherein their produce could be marketed.

The general Enclosure Act of 1845 may be regarded as celebrating the complete disappearance of the open-field farming in Britain.[1]  A result was to give the land-lords a more personal interest in the working of the land, and to encourage an agricultural progress which was not possible under the traditional system.

The beginning of the nineteenth century was to see the introduction of quite another source of food for the farm stock.  Already small quantities of malt combs, brewers' waste, pulpy oil press messes not used as manure were providing " artificial " forage.  The invention of the Bramah press in 1796 resulted in providing much vegetable refuse which could be made into dry cakes suitable for transport and storage.  The first cakes were made from linseed and rape seed, both

_____
[1] There are still one or two places where it lingers as a " quaint " survival.

undecorticated, and later on decorticated cotton seeds became very popular. By 1870 various nuts, palm kernels, and sesame cake, generally mixed with other foodstuff to form a compound cake, had become a well-recognized item of the dietary. By 1880, grain had so fallen in price that it was being fed to cattle, and in due course, after the invention of drying machinery, dried grains, dried blood, dried fish, etc., were all employed in the same way. Now that railway facilities have made transport easy, even potatoes are fed to cows in over-plentiful seasons.

The increased quantity and variety of food in the form of cakes and concentrates has brought about a further change in stock-keeping. The fattening of the older stock continues, though there is nowadays a decided liking for baby beef and young meat, but young stock can be grown and fattened simultaneously, so that it may be sent with profit to the butcher at fifteen or eighteen months.

## CHAPTER X

THE PASTORAL REVOLUTION—2. THE MAKING OF
THE BREEDS

THE introduction of better feeding crops may be
regarded as the first step in the pastoral revolution of the eighteenth century; the second was to
evolve an animal worthy of its food.

With regard to cattle it is generally admitted that
purely British breeds are descended from two types :
a long-horned breed introduced or pastured by the
Celts, and a medium-horned introduced by the Teutons.
In a general way the Celtic strain is still to be found in
the west and north-west of Britain, and the Teutonic
in the east and south-east. Some differentiation in these
two breeds and certain later immigrations, such as the
importation of Frisians and Low Country cattle during
and after the sixteenth century had so wrought upon
the cattle of Britain, that at the moment that second
step, referred to above, was about to be taken, they
were particularly unfixed in type, displaying all colours,
all patterns, Celtic or Roman influence making for long,
wavy horns, and Norse for big bellies, short legs, lightish
colours, and no horns, and Dutch for a general increase
in size. The descendants of the Norse cattle appear to
have been found all round our coast lands and on our
smaller islands, but by the eighteenth century the Norse
strain had died out, except in north-eastern Scotland,
Galloway, and East Anglia, where they had finally
developed into the well-known hornless Aberdeen-Angus,
Galloways, and Red Polled Cattle of Norfolk and Suffolk.

With regard to sheep it may be conceded that the special influence of soil, climate, and geographical configuration had been at work here also upon the few indigenous breeds, to produce great diversity of type. Practical differences centred round such matters as quality and length of wool, tastiness of flesh, late or early maturity.  During the second half of the eighteenth century the decline in the price of wool, and the necessity for an increased meat output, marked out at least one line upon which a profitable change might be effected in the breeding of sheep.

The first person to make any important and widely recognized experiments upon sheep breeding was a certain Robert Bakewell (1725–95) of Dishley, near Loughborough, in Leicestershire.  Not very much is known about the life of this great man.  His father was for a long time tenant of the Grange Farm, near Loughborough, and had travelled much and far to collect animals of the best stock available for his breeding experiments.  In 1760 the younger Bakewell inherited this farm and continued his father's work.  His maxims " small in size, great in value ", " symmetry, well covered ", reflect a criticism upon the ideals of the stockbreeders of his time.  Exact details of the methods by which he effected permanent improvement in the breed are not known, though undoubtedly good feeding played its part.  The general lines upon which he worked have been epitomized in three or four axioms, of which the first, " like begets like ", needs no explanation.  That " form should be related to function " signifies that a small-boned animal of barrel form (symmetry) was likely to have a larger proportion of flesh and lower proportion of offal or waste product than the ungainly, large-boned beasts that had become the stockbreeders' ideal. Bakewell also held that the quality of the meat depended

on the breed rather than on the size of the animal or
its food, and that early maturity producing youngish
meat on good-sized joints could be secured by careful
breeding.  To obtain these desirable qualities matings
must be " in-and-in " ; that is, once a good experimental flock or herd had been built up, the matings
must take place within the group even to the closest
relationships.  Such in-breeding eliminated the chance
of uncertainty in the progeny.

Bakewell's experiments were based mainly upon improving the native Leicester sheep and the long-horned
cattle of the English Midlands.  His first step was to
secure a good flock or herd whose members possessed
as many of the required characteristics as possible.  He
selected from the different flocks and herds of his neighbourhood sheep or cattle possessed of the most perfect
symmetry attainable, the greatest aptitude to fatten,
and a size rather below that of the stock generally bred
at that time.  It is possible that a little " Lincoln "
blood was added to the " Leicester " blood of the home
flock, but from Canley near Coventry, and from Westmorland, he obtained in the one case two heifers and
in the other a bull whose " blood " contributed much
to the building up of his herd of longhorn cattle.  By
renting his rams and bulls for the season to neighbouring farmers he was able to keep a large number of
males and also to observe the quality of their offspring,
thus being in a position to determine and select only
the best males for use upon his experimental stock.
When his best sheep and cattle were past service they
were fattened for the butcher, and rumour had it that
Bakewell infected them before sale with some disease
to prevent their buyers using them for further breeding.

The traditional " old " Leicester was a big—but
somewhat coarse-woolled—sheep of ungainly body and

late maturity. The " new " Leicester was smaller, more symmetrical, of better fattening propensities and of earlier maturity. The establishment of the " breed " was so complete that 100 years later the " new " Leicester sheep had undergone hardly any change. With cattle Bakewell was less successful. The improved longhorn soon passed out of favour, its length of horn making it troublesome in a farmyard, but the experiments had proved conclusively that animals with special characteristics could be produced by careful selection [1] of sire and dam followed by in-breeding to fix the type. Of course, as the members of the herd increased in numbers, union could take place between more distant affinities without loss of type.

Farmers attending the markets at Derby and Loughborough heard accounts of the Dishley breeding successes, and men flocked from all parts of the kingdom to inspect the stock and glean what information they could. But the high prices demanded for use of the Dishley animals (which in later years reached 500 guineas for the season's use of a ram), and the secrecy maintained upon the more practical details, roused the envy and opposition of the less successful livestock farmers and a great campaign was set on foot against the Dishley methods. Arguing by human analogy, even in the face of successful experiment, it was held that the in-and-in breeding must produce weaker stock, and, further, that it was against religion and nature! On the commercial side the attack was delivered against the smaller size of the new breed. The defence easily showed that the smaller, or at any rate more compact, framework carried a greater proportionate amount of meat than in the case of the larger animal, besides needing less food. However, a modified form of this

[1] " Best to best."

excessive in-breeding became and remains quite common : this is *line* breeding, or mating between animals of the same family strain, though not closely related.

Bakewell defended his methods and perhaps fortified them by founding the Dishley Club, whose twelve members swore upon their honour to keep the transactions secret, and to maintain purity of breed in their stock-farming.  No member of the Club might sell lambs for breeding unless he sold the whole flock, or to another member.  No member could lease out more than thirty rams a year or deal with flock-masters showing rams in the market, or with members of the Lincoln Society (Lincoln sheep being powerful rivals of the new Leicesters) unless four members united to pay 200 guineas for its hire.

Once established, the new Leicesters immediately became the foundation for many other improvements in the breeds of British sheep, and the first of these new breeds is bound up with the name of the Culley brothers.  These young men farmed land near Wooler in Northumberland, not far from the Cheviot border, where the long-woolled local sheep were of the Teeswater and Cheviot breeds.  The two Culleys spent some time in Leicestershire, and became great admirers of Bakewell's sheep.  On returning home (1767) they took with them some Leicester rams, and mated them with selected ewes from the local breeds.  Continuing to use the Leicester rams on these ewes and their descendants by the in-breeding method, they obtained and fixed a type of sheep to which they gave the appropriate name of Border Leicester.  The Border Leicester is bolder and more stylish in appearance than the English Leicester and gives finer and more tasty mutton, an inheritance from Cheviot ancestry.  Turnip husbandry, which had just been developed in the district, played its part in the making of the new breed, and has continued a recognized factor in the Border Leicester dietary.

The Border Leicester was introduced to the Border Lowlands at a time when pioneer farming was in the process of transforming barren wastes into good pastures or corn lands. The new sheep and the stock bred from it were exactly adapted to the new system, and it has been said on good authority that agriculture could hardly have developed in the Scottish Lowlands without it. This useful breed spread rapidly over the low grounds north to Caithness and south to Yorkshire.

While the New Leicester and Border Leicester were being evolved in the Midlands and North of England, another revolutionary change was taking place in the South. This change is associated with the names of Robert Ellman, of Glynde, near Lewes, in Sussex, and Jonas Webb, of Babraham, Cambridge.

Ellman succeeded to his father's farm in 1780, and began work similar to Bakewell's upon the short-woolled, rough hill sheep of the South Downs. His aim was " better mutton ", and he worked upon a sheep whose wool was of good quality, and meat of very fair flavour. The Southdown is a breed of long standing : its habitat was partly on the leguminous and aromatic pastures of the Chalk hills, and partly on the Wealden pastures to which for many centuries the Down breeders wintered or agisted their sheep from October to April. The good quality of wool and meat no doubt owed much to this diversity of environment.

Ellman's breeding stock was obtained by careful selection among the native Sussex sheep, and the matings were generally less close than in the Bakewell experiments, though probably some in-breeding played a part in building up the experimental stock. There exist no particular records of the proceedings, but it

is well known that the new root crops were employed
for providing a regular and nutritious diet, necessitating
both catch cropping and close folding in the farming
methods.

Ellman's experiments were carried out in an almost
ideal environment. A strip of low, cultivated land
extending all along the Sussex Hills, provided the catch
crops needed, especially for the winter, while the daytime régime on the hills gave good pasture in summer.
As a result of this careful management, the aptitude
for close folding is transmitted, and all Down breeds
are well suited to arable farming of this kind, while
the aptitude for early fattening has made the Southdown almost the rival of the Leicester. It must be
kept on the chalk, however, if the type is to be maintained, though it can easily be fattened for the butcher
under special feeding conditions. The Southdown is a
small, hornless sheep, very active and able to roam
far in search of food. The improved Southdown has
always been a favourite stock with Royalty and the
nobility.

In 1829 Ellman's stock of about 4,000 head was
dispersed to become an important basis for the improvement of other breeds.

Jonas Webb began his operations about 1823, when
he purchased a stock of " Ellman " sheep. His aim
was to produce a larger animal, for the country round
Cambridge, where they were to feed, is more fertile
than the Downland country. As in the other cases,
there are no precise records of his working methods,
but his success was such that for many years his
" improved Southdowns " were the most valuable in
the country, and provided a source of reinvigoration
for all the highest-grade flocks. His flock was dispersed
in 1862.

The first to devise improvements both important and lasting in cattle breeds were the brothers Collings, of the County of Durham.  In 1782 Charles, the younger of the two, took over his father's farm at Ketton, near Darlington, and the following year paid a long visit to Bakewell.  The other brother, Robert, after starting in a business career, became tenant of a farm at Barmpton and, like his brother, began to breed cattle for the purpose of improving the shorthorn.

Charles' first acquisition was a bull, chosen because it was " mellow " to the touch, in contrast to the majority of bulls of the day, whose bodies were " hard as a board ".  This was the famous " Hubback ", the father of the breed.  For mothers of his experimental stock, he purchased The Duchess, Cherry, Daisy, and Favourite, all of good ancestry.

The " old " shorthorn was an old-established breed known from the name of the original habitat as Teeswater, Durham, and Holderness cattle.  Along the rich grazing valleys of the Tees noblemen and the local gentry had long been endeavouring to keep up and promote still further the excellence of their herds by good feeding.  About 1700 the then owner of Fountains Abbey and its cattle descended from the white cattle of the former monks, bought bulls from Holland, red, or red and white in colour to mate with his cows.  The offspring of these bulls and cows were generally roan.

The Collings based their experiments upon the old Teeswater breed, whose cow was already recognized to be a deeper milker than the cow of any other breed in the British Isles.  The aim was to obtain greater symmetry in the carcase and reduction of size in the body and horn, there being at that time a great demand for farmyard cows with shorter horns.  He also desired to enhance the qualities of early maturity and good meat already possessed by the old breed.  His methods followed the general lines laid down by Bakewell.  Eleven years after the beginning of his experiments Charles Collings had bred the famous Durham Ox, and the even more famous Comet, which was sold in 1810 for 1,000 guineas.  The progeny of these few animals are now found all the world over.  The milk type has been especially developed in Cumberland, Penrith being a well-known centre for the purchase of dairy shorthorns.

The success of the Collings brothers stimulated others to the good work, dairy shorthorns being especially popular because, when their milking service was over, the cows could be sent to the butcher almost at once, their flesh being fuller and of better beef taste than that of other cows under similar circumstances.  The males on fattening also gave a good flavoured meat.

Among the most noted of the Collings' successors are Thomas Booth of Killerby, near Northallerton, and Thomas Bates of Kirk Levington, near Cleveland.  The former began farming about 1790, having bought freely from the Collings' stock.  These two cattle breeders had very diverse ends in view, Booth breeding for the " butcher ", Bates for the " pail ".  Unfortunately, the extensive close breeding was carried too far and ruined both herds.

The first permanent success in the breeding of shorthorns after the Collings was gained perhaps by Hugh Watson of Keillor in Forfarshire (1789–1865).  To him we owe the great Angus or Forfar breed.[1]

When Watson was but 18 years old he became tenant of Keillor, receiving from his father, tenant of a neighbouring farm, six of his " best and blackest cows " along with a bull as nucleus of his farm stock.  The

---

[1] Three or four years ago Forfarshire resumed its ancient name of Angus.

H

same summer he purchased ten heifers and ten bulls
showing the best characteristics of the breed.  At this
period a black-polled or hornless cattle of the " lower "
or hill country of Forfar and Aberdeen was known in
the two counties as Angus Doddie and Buchan Humlie
respectively (humlie and doddie signifying absence of
horns).  When quite young Hugh Watson had visited
Robert Collings and studied his work at first hand.
Having secured his experimental herd, he, too, went
in for close breeding and good feeding, and for fifty
years each of his stock bulls was succeeded by one or
other of its sons.  His object was a fusion of the Aberdeen and Angus breeds.  By 1810 he was ready to
exhibit, and his success initially at local shows, and
later at the Smithfield Club and the Agricultural and
Highland Society of Scotland, caused his cattle to be
recognized as the best in the county.  Keillor became
the chief centre for stock bulls for the first-class breeders,
who in their turn supplied the lesser men.  Before he
was fifty years old the majority of the black cattle of
Forfarshire and Kincardineshire was descended from
Watson stock.

As there were other well-defined hornless breeds, the
name Aberdeen-Angus was adopted for the black polled
cattle of Keillor stock.

The perfecting of the polled cattle was continued by
William McCombie of Tillyfour (1805–80), who became
the leader of the Aberdeenshire cattle breeders of his
day.  The qualities he sought to perpetuate were absence
of horns, stout body, black colour.  His interest began
with his father's stock of store cattle which, in the
capacity of cattle dealer, he took to various fairs.  In
1830 he became owner of his father's farm.  He bred
from Watson stock, and fixing the desired type by in-
breeding, was instrumental in carrying the Keillor blood

to all parts of Aberdeen and Banffshire.  Indiscriminate crossings with shorthorns had caused the Buchan to be threatened with extinction, but McCombie's efforts, directed to restore and retain the polled cattle of Aberdeen in their purity, removed this danger, and by perpetuating the goodness in the strain, he did more than any of his contemporaries to raise these cattle from a local to a world-wide breed.  The dispersal of McCombie's stock in 1874 and its improved form for breeding purposes enabled the Duke of Richmond to found a herd of polled cattle at Goodwood, Sussex. About this time other men of note and wealth, among whom may be mentioned the Marquis of Huntly, the Earl of Fife, Sir George Macpherson Grant of Ballindalloch, began to take a great interest in breeding polled cattle.  The Ballindalloch stock came from both the Keillor and Tillyfour farms, thus carrying on the work of Watson into the twentieth century.  On the death of these breeders, good Aberdeen-Angus blood was dispersed over wide areas.  By 1880 this breed, also known as Polled Angus, was standardized and taking first prizes in the December fat stock shows of London and Birmingham, and railway transport was permitting a considerable trade in Aberdeen meat for London.

The Aberdeen-Angus cattle are hornless and generally black.  The occasional appearance of red or horned calves marks reversion to not very distant ancestors. Though the cows give a fair quantity of milk, the breed is essentially a good beef breed of early maturity, and is valued for its meat rather than its milk.

The nineteenth century also witnessed the improvement in the Ayrshire cattle, the great milk breed of Scotland.

The districts of Cunningham, Kyle, and Carrick in Ayrshire had produced indigenous breeds of Ayrshires (heard of as Dunlops in 1795). The mild climate and poor thin soil of this county is especially favourable for a hardy milch cow. Cunningham, north of the River Irvine, is regarded as the cradle of the improved Ayrshire Dairy breed. The methods adopted included better feeding and some crossing with a stronger breed (which may have been Teeswater or Dutch), and breeding from selected individuals of the herd. The result was a change in colour and shape, and an increase in the milk yield. The improved breed was introduced into Carrick (South Ayrshire) by a Mr. Fulton, about 1793, and in 1802 the first herd of Ayrshires was established in Wigtownshire, where the breed ultimately wrested much of their pastures from the Galloway cattle. By the end of the century the Ayrshires had spread into Dumfriesshire. The improvement in the type received an impetus from the work of one of the Dukes of Atholl, who, as President of the Highland Society in 1858–61, acquired an interest both in farming and in Ayrshires, urging the importance of keeping pedigree herd books.

The Ayrshires are rather small and red, brown, yellow, or black and white in colour. The cows give large quantities of milk in proportion to the food consumed, and when their milking activities cease, they can be quickly fed up for the butcher, though the Galloway Ayrshires are more fitted for the grazier and butcher than the native-bred Ayrshires. This cow more than any other supplies the ever-growing and not too far distant market for the milk and milk products of the industrial area of south-western Scotland. These cows, introduced into Galloway 1850–70, are to be found to-day all over Britain from Land's End to John o' Groats.

The few breeds whose early history has been touched

upon in this chapter, by no means exhaust the number
of herds of British sheep and cattle. The process of
" improvement " is still going on. But our interest at
this point lies in that first step the success of which would
have seemed miraculous to the farmers of a few generations earlier, and upon whose maxims and methods
most of the subsequent experiments in stock breeding
have been based. Meanwhile we may note how great
is the change that has come over the pastoral scene
since the break-up of the open-field system. *Now* we
can have fresh meat and milk all the year round, and
cattle may be reared not only for milk but for meat,
giving this preferred flavour or that. But our present
excellence in stock breeding (that is to say, when breeders
give sufficient care) did not come all at once—like the
breeds the ideals had to undergo a slow " improvement ". The desiderata of the early experiments were
often comic. For a time size was the only criterion of
merit. " Nothing would please but elephants or giants,"
wrote Culley in 1786, and there is a story of an ox taken
round the country for example and admiration whose
monstrous proportions required a species of coach-cage,
the animal not being able to walk more than a few
steps without assistance !

During the eighteenth century the science of stock
breeding mastered the main essentials, but that of the
nineteenth aimed at a still more universal prevalence
of good type. With this end in view there have been
established Herd and Flock Books, Clubs of various
kinds, and competitions and prizes at annual or seasonal
fairs and shows. The lines along which improvement
is sought include proportion of meat to bone, quality
and flavour of flesh, early maturity, quantity and
quality of milk, wool, etc. Finally, it may be said
with confidence, that none of the earlier experiments

which have rendered the later ones possible could have
been initiated or carried out by a peasantry working
on the open-field system, or a smallholder, however
independent, farming up to a subsistence level that
would not permit any risks being taken.   Only the large
landowners, from duke to baronet, from squire to
gentleman, or the rich tenant farmers, could have taken
the earlier steps in this great pastoral revolution, being
able to survive both risk and failure and having the
leisure to devise experiments, and the means to carry
them out.

## CHAPTER XI

## THE AID OF APPLIED SCIENCE—1. RECLAMATION

IN this and the following chapter, we shall consider some methods of applied science whereby additional land was gained by reclamation and irrigation for the cultivation of forage crops, pastures were created out of waste, and existing pastures improved.

Reclamation of swamps and marshes was begun under the Roman régime, but our earliest large-scale drainage operations date from the sixteenth and seventeenth centuries, their success being due to Dutch ingenuity. Wapping Marsh was reclaimed by Cornelius Vanderdelf in 1544, and the draining of the Plumstead and Greenwich Marshes was also begun in the reign of Henry VIII. The great reclamation triumphs, however, were concerned with the Humber lands and the Fen District.

The Humber lands were drained under the direction of Cornelius Vermuyden in 1642. The reclamation extended over much of the Isle of Axholme, traversed in changing meanders by the rivers Don, Torne, and Idle. By drains and dyking the old Don was made to enter the Ouse directly, instead of by way of the Aire, and the Idle and Torne, the first named an eastern tributary of the old Don, and the second tributary to the Idle by two heads, were both directed in straighter courses to the Trent. Smaller drains at right angles to these assisted the general drainage, and sluices placed where the main drains entered the rivers kept out the tidal waters. The scheme involved embanking the Trent and erecting pumping mills where the gradient otherwise

was too slight to keep the water in continual movement. In the eighteenth century the drainage was
improved and extended, steam pumps replacing horse
or wind-worked pumps. The reclaimed land is still
prone to flooding. Cattle predominate here, and where
the land is sufficiently dry for agriculture, the produce
finds a market in the neighbouring industrial region.

The Fens formerly extended into the six counties of
Cambridge, Lincoln, Huntingdon, Northampton, Suffolk, and Norfolk. In the time of the Romans much
of the coastline here consisted of rather wide, but
shallow inlets, into which flowed sluggish silt-laden
streams. Twice a day the tidal water forced back the
river water which, overflowing its low banks, spread
out as a vast, shallow bay dotted with a few islands of
glacial gravels rising on a rock foundation whereon the
early inhabitants had made settlements. The first
attempts at reclamation consisted in the few dykes and
ditches constructed by the Romans ; the subsequent
silting of the rivers in their lower courses, the growth of
water weeds and peat formations converted this territory into a wilderness of bogs, pools, and reedy shoals,
with firmer ground in places.

The true fenland peat area was bordered seaward by
a wide belt of silt, and landward by a belt of boulder
clay. Here and there, and especially in the south, are
outcrops of Jurassic rock which from the seventh century onwards were utilized by the monks for the erec-
tion of their " houses " in localities free from the distrac-
tion of the civil disturbances of those times. To obtain
food supplies the fen adjacent to these " islands " was
extensively cultivated, while the dry season provided
additional summer pasture. During the eleventh century Richard de Rulos [1] carried out some reclamation

[1] E. H. Darby, *Geographical Journal*, Nov. 1932.

along the Welland Valley in the peat fen ; the success
of this effort stimulated others. The silt and clayey
land of the north and centre is less liable to the annual
flooding except on the seaward margin, and so more
suited for human settlement. The seasonal rise and fall
of the water level in the Fens left a broad zone of summer
pasture, flooded in winter, and as reclamation pro-
gressed round the different centres, the pasture became
at once easier of access and of longer annual use.

By the twelfth century stock-raising had become one
of the most important occupations of the Fens, cattle
feeding on the damper and sheep on the drier of the
released pastures. The permanently reclaimed land
was used for arable farming. The cattle of each little
settlement were pastured in common, a procedure which
established in some districts pasture rights still in existence. The salt wind from the sea enhanced the excellence of these feeding grounds.

The population of the true fen lived by fishing and
fowling, keeping geese and cutting willows and reeds for
thatching, litter, basket-making, etc., and peat for fuel.
Salt could be prepared easily. Travelling about the
district was done in punts or on stilts, according to the
complete or partial immersion.

Some further reclamation was instituted by John
Morton, Bishop of Ely, on his return from exile in
Flanders (1485), where he had been much struck with
the system of water drainage. " Morton's Leam " still
takes part in the draining operations of our English Fens.

During the reign of Henry VIII a number of Acts provided for reclamation of marshes and fens by " under-
takers " who were paid for their work by allotment of
one-half or one-third of the reclaimed land, according to
their outlay. By 1607 a great deal of " firme land " had
been won through the simple expedients of ditch and

bank construction, the necessary pumping power being
supplied by horses.   Breaches in the sea-wall were frequent, when much cattle and corn land was destroyed,
disasters which brought the district to the attention of
men in high places.   In 1630 a private company of local
magnates began reclamation upon what is known as
the Bedford Level.   A "Commission of Sewers" was
formed and Sir Cornelius Vermuyden, the famous Dutch
engineer, put in charge.   The fourth Earl of Bedford
was Chairman of this "Company of Adventurers", but
the outbreak of the Civil War put a stop to the reclamations, which were resumed, however, after 1649 under
the chairmanship of the fifth Earl of Bedford.   The
difficulties of the draining were increased by the action
of the fenmen, or commoners, who had no desire to see
their traditional fen occupations destroyed, and realized
that much of the reclaimed land would be alienated
from them.   They therefore filled in the ditches and
broke down the banks whenever opportunity offered.
The presence of foreign workmen was an added source
of irritation.

Vermuyden's general method was to make straight
cuts to shorten the rivers, minor drains, arranged in
herring-bone pattern, also feeding them.   The most
important part of the work was connected with the
Old and New Bedford Rivers, which divert the Ouse
at Earith, and run straight to Denver, where a sluice
gate keeps the tide-water out of the old Ouse, and sends
it up the new cuts, where it spreads out between them.
Pumps worked by windmills were used where necessary.
As the drainage went on roads began to replace the
shallow water-ways, and the areas of reed and sedge
were steadily reduced till they were restricted to the
unreclaimed meres, of which the last, Whittlesea Mere,
was not reclaimed until the nineteenth century.   The

work occupied about four years, producing the 100,000
acres of permanently reclaimed territory known as the
Bedford Level. Acts of Parliament had provided for
the recognition of the rights of the commoners, but the
large amount of land allotted to the Adventurers displaced many of the previous holders. French Adventurers or Dutch Protestants settled there in numbers as
tenant farmers or smallholders ; the high value of the
drained land, the expenses of draining and the character
of the soil all pointed to exploitation by intensive agriculture rather than pasturage. The loss of their swamps
with their rights of turf-cutting, fishing, and fowling,
and the loss, too, of previous pasture rights, were very disastrous for those fenmen who received no, or inadequate,
compensation, neither did they wish to breed bullocks nor
rear sheep for the newcomers, whom they regarded as
usurpers. The result was a prolonged period of riots,
ceasing only in 1714, when much of the reclaimed land
of the Fen district had relapsed to swamps and marsh,
and was restored to the fenmen. This restoration may
have been due, in part, to the difficulty of keeping in
working order such drainage as was in operation, owing
to the still continuing silt deposits. In the eighteenth
century interest was once more aroused in these reclamations. New works were devised on the catch-water
principle, that is, water from the uplands was caught
before getting to the lowlands, and led by contour canals
to the nearest outfall. This new drainage system made
it possible to restore the older one. The engineer Ren-
nie (1761–1821) was largely responsible for the work.

To-day water is lifted into the channels by steam
pumps, but the draining remains difficult, and probably
always will be so, for the rivers still continue to deposit
their silt. An extensive scheme to improve existing
conditions is in progress. At present only two or three

small areas of the original fen remain : e.g., the Wicken
Fen, about 13 miles from Cambridge.

To-day in late summer-time these reclaimed fenlands
are ablaze with yellow corn, and our interest therefore
lies in the root and grass crops and the sheep and cattle-
keeping associated with the rotation. Near the coast
summer pastures give good grazing for sheep and cattle,
the latter predominating, since the damper parts are
not suitable for sheep, and the neighbouring uplands
can take sheep more profitably than cattle. Attention
has been called to the fact that the winter fattening of
sheep and cattle in fold and stall on the adjacent boulder
clay (with its turnip husbandry) is now on the decline,
but the large amount of land under the plough made
it (or did make it) more economical to feed livestock
purchased from other regions, though some, of course,
are entirely local. Hence the tradition for " flying
flocks ". It has been suggested that the pastures could
give better return were dairy cattle substituted for meat
cattle. When not laid down to grass the land is
utilised for intensive agriculture—grain, market-garden-
ing produce, sugar-beet (providing a pulp for cattle
food) and potatoes (especially on the silt lands, or
Holland) are some of the crops grown.

The two examples of the Humber lands and Fens by
no means exhaust the reclamations undertaken in this
country. In many of our river valleys and along our
coasts much waste land has been and more may yet be
reclaimed for pasture. The valley of the Parret provides a notable example. At the time of King Alfred
the plain of Somerset was an almost impassable swamp,
much of it aptly described by the name of Sedgemoor.
The Sedgemoor bog has now been drained and has
become prosperous farming land, especially for cattle.
The draining of the Pevensey Level and Romney Marsh,

begun under the Romans, has given grazing grounds predominantly for cattle in the one case and sheep in the other. The careful draining of the Marsh has removed fear of foot-rot for sheep, and the amount of running water available in the Level provides good drinking, and hence favours the establishment of cattle as the main tenants. Some pastures require continual drainage, especially where a porous surface is underlain by a wet subsoil. Field draining by means of a system of parallel underground ditches was advocated by Blith and Worlidge in the seventeenth century, but was little practised. Later improvements involved tile-lined trenches with stubble, fern, or brushwood infillings. By 1850 a more complete field draining using tiles and cylindrical pipes had become widespread.

Here and there along our coasts are to be found special pastures generally known as *saltings*. The saltings are covered more or less by the tides, especially the spring high tides. The saltings of the Fens have been caused by the tidal waters which sweep in from the north and east, bringing with them suspended silt, rolling up gravel over the adjacent flats, and finally dropping part of their load beyond the reach of the withdrawing motion of the less powerful ebb tides. The growth of samphire here checks the flowing of the water and helps to bind together the deposited material, thus making the ground sufficiently firm for the growth of other plants. The peculiar herbage of these and similar saltings, some of which are found along the mouth of the Thames estuary, gives excellent pasturage for sheep in spite of the water which must collect not far underground. The salt in the soil and herbage renders these saltings very healthy, and sick sheep are put upon them to recover.

Warping is a method of reclamation by means of which a dry surface is created by the deposition of sand

or silt upon an area prepared to receive it.   Water is led
over the " ground " and the reduction of its velocity
causes the suspended material to be " thrown down ".
The word " warp " is said to be akin to the German
word *werfen*, to throw.   In Northumberland moles are
often called warps, because they throw up soil from
underneath ;   timber is said to be warped when it
develops a "throw " in the wrong direction; the throw
of the shuttle in weaving is across the foundation known
as the warp ; and the precipitation of suspended material
in tidal waters is known as warping, the precipitated
mud being called " warp ".   In England the main territory gained from the sea by warping lies along the
Humber and its tributaries, the Trent, Ouse, and Don.
About 1760 the fertility of the sediment deposited by
tidal waters during high tide was recognized as capable
of producing luxuriant corn crops, and a certain farmer
appears to have obtained permission to make a short
tunnel in the embankments of Hatfield Chase (reclaimed
1626) in order to warp his lands.   Ralph Creyke, of
Rawcliffe, near Goole, about 1821 constructed a canal
which carried the warp waters three miles inland, an
operation which may be regarded as the first attempt
at English artificial warping.

The Humber receives continually a yellow mud consisting of the river silt of its tributaries, and the till
or waste from the crumbling Holderness coast which
the tides sweep into the estuary.   Coming from many
rock measures, this fine mud or warp is of great fertility.   The tides churn it up in the estuary, and carry
it in large quantities up the streams they enter.

The process of warping consists in deflecting the high-
tide surplus waters into main canals, from which they
pass into subsidiary canals, and finally into prepared
embanked compartments lying below high-water level.

Here the sediment slowly settles, after which the water is gently drained off between the ebbing of one tide and the flowing of the next.  Without going into technical details, it may be said that care is taken to inundate the entire surface in such a way that the sediment is deposited evenly.  The river adjoining the area to be reclaimed is carefully embanked, so that neither the tidal waters from downstream nor the flood waters from upstream can overflow on to the warplands when not required.  Generally two sluice gates in this embankment are sufficient to regulate the incoming and outgoing water, the high-level gate admitting the water, and the low-level gate, which somewhat resembles a swing door, allowing it to drain off quietly into the ebb.  Every precaution is taken not to disturb the sediment during the draining away, the exit sluice often being so constructed that the water passes out from its upper surface only.  At full tide the flood gates are opened by hydraulic or other power, and the water is liberated on the compartment at its highest level.  As the tide falls, hydrostatic pressure from the water in the compartments pushes riverwards upon the sluice gate, which opens and lets the water out.  The works are extensive, involving high banking of rivers and compartments, main and subsidiary canals and trenches, while in some cases it has been necessary to construct tunnels.  The great extent of land to be warped may necessitate a main canal of several miles length from the initial intake.

The compartments range in size from a few to 400 acres, the tidal waters often entering the larger compartments by two or more sluice gates, in order that the sedimentation may be as far as possible of the same thickness and quality.  The higher the tide, the greater the amount of sedimentation per tide, though the thickness of the warp deposited never exceeds $\frac{1}{8}$ inch and is often much less. Three to four years are required to give a depth of soil of about $3\frac{1}{2}$ feet. During the winter months the rivers contain too much water in proportion to warp and consequently warping is not carried on at this season. The spring tides contain more warp than the corresponding neap tides, as they bring up more water from the Humber and the greater scour of the tides stirs up more warp from the Humber bed.

Warping is begun about the middle of June and continues through the summer, the water being generally admitted at each tide. A good season will give one foot rise, and in low situations much more.

As *soil* is given to the land and the warp supplies all the fertility, the nature of the underlying foundation does not matter so much, and the warping can be successfully applied to peatland, bogland, sandy, and clay soils. Warpland should, however, be kept well drained, and hence peat makes a good subsoil. Peat moss is, in fact, the land most frequently improved by warping. The fine texture of the warp, without stones and close-grained, can ultimately produce extensive crops, but when first deposited it is rather brackish. When the deposition is finished a season is allowed for settlement, after which the ground is raised into ridges of about four yards wide and sown with grass in spring. This grass provides grazing for two years or more, by which time the salt has disappeared and cultivation can begin. This pasture prologue is of immense value in desalting and manuring the soil in preparation for future agriculture, especially potato growing. When reclamation is complete, where desired the ground gives fattening pastures of high quality and is mainly used as such for the Lincoln Red shorthorns. After an interval of from five to ten years a second warping is often necessary to put the finishing touches to the reclamation.

Another example of successful warping, albeit one much smaller in scale, is that of the Cherry Cobsands, where the warp stratum is said to be four yards thick.

An interesting account of an early experiment in warping is related by William Tatham, in his book on *National Irrigation*, 1801. A certain James Templer, of the parish of Teignmouth, in Devon, exported the clay of his estates to Liverpool and elsewhere to pottery works. He first built a canal which took the clay to Teignmouth for shipment, and later hit upon the idea of diverting its surplus water, due to the winter floods, over some marshy land adjoining the lower reaches of his canal. " Well contrived " sluice gates placed in the canal wall admitted the water where desired into a net-work of trenches of gradually decreasing width. En-riched with slime from the high grounds, these flood waters built up the soil so that presently it was possible to convert the marshes into green meadows. The suc-cess was such that farmers who had unwillingly paid 10*s.* per acre for the season's pasturage gladly paid £2 or even £8 after the reclamation.

CHAPTER XII

## THE AID OF APPLIED SCIENCE—2. IRRIGATION

AT first sight it would hardly seem that the mild climate and well-distributed rainfall of Britain would necessitate irrigation, but the beneficent action upon grassland of flowing water has long been recognized. The additional water, through seepage or mists, that makes the grass of water meadows more luscious than that of fields receiving the same rainfall, must have been noticed by the very earliest of our farming people. It has been claimed that our irrigation works go back to Roman times, though the evidence supporting this claim is decidedly shadowy and appears to be based partly on the assumption that no good or new thing could come out of Celtic or Saxon farming.[1] It has also been held that most of our water meadows were the work of Dutch engineers, but their efforts were chiefly confined to the Humber lands and the Fen district, while the earlier irrigation in South Britain was more or less restricted to our southern counties. In the absence of more definite testimony, something might be left, perhaps, to the native genius of the British farmer.

The annals of the reign of Queen Elizabeth hint at this method of watering pastures, but there were no

[1] King, writing in 1911, stated that the old English water meadows are chiefly in the vicinity of Roman stations ; but many of these sites, for geographical and political reasons, had been occupied earlier by Celtic settlements and were revived later by the Angles and Saxons. Hints of early " flooding " that come from former Caledonia show it was not only the Romans who realized the value of artificial watering.

definite records on the subject until the latter half of
the seventeenth century. This may not mean very
much, however—even in the celebrated Domesday
Survey there were very important omissions regarding
our northern counties.

By 1669 the method of improving pasture grass by
" floating " or " drowning " was an established factor.
Sward produced by a soaking in stagnant water is
rather coarse and unnutritious, but if moving or flowing
water be substituted the results are very different.
The irrigation was effected by diverting a stream over
the grassland, or by pumping water into a system of
trenches from a main trench, the trenches becoming
more numerous and shallower until the water was
distributed all over the area. A counter system of
drainage trenches in the lower part of the field collected
and removed the water after use. When fully
elaborated, the most popular methods of irrigation of
pastures were the ridge and furrow, or bed-work system,
and the catch water system.

The ridge and furrow system is peculiarly useful when
the land to be watered is fairly level. A canal takes off
from a river and carries the water to the prepared area
situated at a level lower than the canal intake. By
means of a dam and sluice gate this canal delivers the
water into a trench that runs more or less along the top
of the area to be watered, but with a slight adjustment
to give it a fall equal to the gradient of the river downstream. The ground is flung up into ridges which in the
typical case should lie parallel to each other and at right
angles to the main conductor or carrier just mentioned.
The tops of the ridges are grooved along their length
with little trenches or gutters which are supplied from
the main conductor. The furrows or troughs between
the ridges carry the draining gutters, each of which lies,

in the typical case, at right angles to the main drain that takes the water back to the stream, either directly, or through some other drain at some distance below the intake of the canal. The object of the gradients is to provide a steady flow of water by the action of gravity. Both the feeding and draining gutters taper slightly towards their free end and also become progressively shallower outwards along their length. This tapering and shallowing of the feeding gutters assists in drawing the water to the outward end during the filling process, and when full, in promoting overflow in a thin but even sheet so that the slopes of the ridges are uniformly watered. The similar arrangement of the draining gutters, which are deepest where the feeding gutters are shallowest and therefore retain the least water, prevents the lower slopes from getting excess, and assists the draining of the gutters into the main draining trench when the watering is over. When the irrigation is finished a sluice gate closes the dam, and the slightly sloping bed of the feeding gutters enables the water left in them to run direct into the main conductor; their intakes are then closed by means of a piece of turf, stone, or board. A subsidiary sluice gate enables this main conductor to be drained back into the canal. In this way the meadow is soon dried.

In actual practice the ridges are rarely so regular, and " stops " are at times used in the feeding gutters to assist the regularity of the overflow, and to enable the meadow to be watered in sections if required. This system can still be studied along the Test and Itchen Rivers in Hampshire, the Avon, Kennet and Wily [1] in Wiltshire, and elsewhere. The operation was, and is, generally in the hands of an irrigating official known according to locality as the drowner, meadman, etc.;

[1] Initiated 1700–5, according to Tatham.

he selects the portion of the meadow to be irrigated, the time and duration of the operation, and supervises the general upkeep of the system, a matter of no great expense, since once constructed the ridges and troughs may be regarded as comparatively permanent. The use of a good-sized stream is necessary.

A less expensive system to initiate is that of the catch water system. This method is very appropriate where ground slopes rather steeply, especially if it face the sun. It is also suitable for small areas. The source of water is a spring, or small stream, from which water can be taken at a level somewhat higher than the top of the ground to be irrigated, and carried in a canal of small gradient to a point where it can be admitted into a conductor or trench that runs along the top of the field. When full the trench overflows along its length or a portion of it regulated by " stops " of turf, etc., the water running down the slope in a uniform sheet. The bed of this conductor both tapers and shallows along its length outward from the point of entry of the water, and a downward turn at the free end, as also in the case of the ridge gutters of the other system, sometimes assists the even spreading of the overflow. Water on a slope, however, tends sooner or later to collect in little rills, due mainly to the irregularities of the ground, slight though these may be, whereby part of the grassland would remain dry. To prevent this, when still moving evenly the overflow is trapped by a second, though smaller, trench or gutter, constructed more or less along a contour and possibly provided with its stops similar to the main conductor. Similar parallel gutters extend down the whole slope, the water falling into, filling up, and overflowing from each in turn. The lowest gutter collects all the water and either becomes the main conductor for another field, or returns the water to the river.  Final draining of the parallel trenches and gutters is affected by a deep drain cut at right angles to these others, and extending from the top to the bottom of the system.

It is obvious that the grass between the upper gutters will probably receive more of the " richness " carried by the stream water than those lower down.  This disadvantage is sometimes obviated by use of a median trench, leading from the main conductor and cutting all the hillside gutters at right angles.  Regulators or dams of turf, etc., can keep the water from this trench out of the upper gutters, so that the lower ones receive the " good water " more directly.  This median trench is susceptible of many variations, which include complete diversion of the whole of the feeding stream for a part of its course.  Feeding trenches may run out from it at right angles, each supplying a little group of parallel gutters.

The catch water system was and is particularly used in Devon.  The initial outlay is small, the gutters being shallow and easily turned by the plough.  Much furze-brake on the hill-slopes of North Devon has been converted by these means into valuable grassland.  In Wiltshire and in other places, including Scotland, the two systems are sometimes combined.

The essential factor in the ridge and furrow and the catch water systems of irrigation is the continual movement of the water.  The flowing sheet aerates the soil, feeds the vegetation through the material suspended or dissolved in it, and in winter, when properly applied, prevents frost from reaching the roots.

The routine of the ridge and furrow drowning was somewhat as follows.  About the middle of October, when the grass had been eaten bare, the drowner did the repairs necessitated by the trampling of cattle, the choking of gutters with rank grass, etc.   The work was first carried out over a section of the field designated a " pitch of work ", and then the pitch was watered while another section of the field was being repaired.   In Gloucester and Wiltshire the waters arising from the first heavy rains after Michaelmas were considered particularly efficacious, because they contained the washings from the arable lands on the chalk hills and dust, horse-dung, etc., from the roads.   All through October till and including January the soaking continued, the water flowing over the beds from two to three weeks at a stretch, with a day's interval now and again to prevent the grass from becoming coarse and the ground boggy. After the January soaking the ground was completely drained to encourage the grass, and left dry until the growth showed signs of flagging, when watering was continued for a few days at a time with complete drying in between.   The appearance of a white scum giving warning that drying was needed was often formed in February, whereupon the customary amount of water given was halved.   If frost came during the dry period, watering was suspended, lest the soil should freeze and the roots be injured.   If frost came during a watering it was continued even if it were time for drying the field ; in this case the moving water, being above the temperature of ice, protected the roots.

The object of all this care was to obtain " early grass " for " early " lambs.   An acre of good meadow grass, prepared thus, could take 500 ewes and their lambs. These water meads were used until the barley sowing was ended.[1]

In Gloucester this spring feed under meadow irrigation was given as early as 1789 to " hard-wintered " cattle

[1] See p. 7.   The ewes and lambs eat off the pastures in much the same way now as formerly.

and sheep, and as a consequence cheese-making was put forward a month, and even at this date there was some lamb fattening.

The repairing precautions and general routine of the catch water system followed much the same plan as the one outlined above. The trenches and gutters were cleaned out and repaired in November and use was made of the first winter showers in order to secure the muddy water for the manurial value of its suspended material. The water was turned on for a stretch of three weeks, as in the other system, etc.

Previous to 1801 the catch water irrigation appears to have been attempted at Osbournby in Lincolnshire on poor sandy soil. As a result sedge was destroyed, and white clover grown instead (Tatham).

Early irrigation in Scotland consisted mainly in a partial wetting of the land, and apparently was confined to the two shires of Lanark and Perth. In 1792 a certain Charles Stephens was engaged by the Highland Society to make a general survey of the country with a view to a more scientific development of irrigation. A consequence of this survey and the encouragement and advice offered by Stephens was the initiation of small local irrigation schemes to add to the pastoral resources in grass and hay in the shires of Caithness, Clackmannan, Peebles, Perth, Wigtown, and Aberdeen : in Aberdeenshire heath moor was permanently transformed into better heath and good grassland. These enterprises were undertaken by landowning magnates from duke to mere gentleman, but though the reclamation affected much hitherto worthless land, the small farmers were suspicious of its utility and held aloof. Possibly they could not afford the time of waiting or the undoubted failures that now and again occurred. For example, the Duke of Buccleuch, a most progressive irrigator, pro-

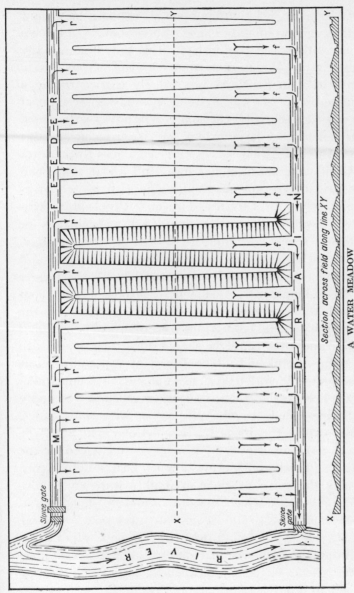

A WATER MEADOW

Diagrammatic sketch of Ridge and Furrow Irrigation : r = ridge, or feeding gutters ; f = furrow, or draining gutters.
In this diagram only the central section shows in full detail the shading of the feeding gutters to indicate where the water falls into the draining gutters : but, as reference to the section shows, the operation is the same throughout the map.

posed to institute irrigation upon his estates if his tenant
farmers, who would later benefit therefrom, would agree
to pay interest on the outlay.   This they unanimously
refused to do, threatening to give up their farms first.

Irrigation in Scotland was usually carried on by a
combination of the two systems, possibly on account of
the varied surface of the land.   The areas so watered
were not of very large extent, varying from one to fifty
acres (Duke of Atholl, 1827).   A certain Miss Rutherford,
of Glendevon, farming her own land about 1828, had
two irrigated meadows of nine and two Scotch acres
respectively.   In Dumfriesshire and Peeblesshire irrigated meadow hay was considered as valuable for
fattening sheep and bullocks as the best clover hay.

The enthusiasm for irrigation both in England and
Scotland rose high, and penetrated beyond the farmer
to the administrative councils.   Tatham (1801) considered that vagrants and disorderly classes of the
community should be employed on " national irrigation "
works, and that convicts should turn their energies to
the same useful end.   The Board of Agriculture sent
circulars to the various canal companies, then flourishing
greatly, requesting them to consider schemes " to apply
navigable canals to the purpose of irrigating land ".

Meanwhile the irrigators could not agree upon the
actual cause or degree of beneficence conferred by the
irrigating flood, and there was much heated debate concerning the value of clear or muddy water.

The means by which meadows should be flooded and
drained are still undergoing investigation.   A very
modern method is to lay down underground pipes fitted
at intervals with vertical shafts.   Water is supplied
from trenches at the top of the field, and by using strong
sluices to stop the drainage outlet at the bottom, the
water is forced up these shafts and floods the meadows.

It can be drawn off when desired by opening the sluices. This device enables more of the field to get a " direct " watering.

From 1760 onwards the making of good grassland and reclaiming of waste for forage crops received assistance from a very unexpected quarter. For some time past the standard of living had been rising in all settled branches of society, and with this increase in comfort came the desire for more healthy homes and villages. Up to this time the domestic and livestock waste had been disposed of by the most casual methods, such as open drains or ditches in the streets, cesspools, etc., much of this material being carried by surface flow or underground seepage to the neighbouring streams.

Besides the unpleasantness of overflowing drains in the wet season and noxious vapours in the dry, it was undeniable that this method of disposal of the community waste polluted the streams to a less or greater extent, sometimes with much danger to health and life.

The first truly scientific attempt to render such material harmless was that of devising some means to purify the sewage water before it drained into the river, and the method selected was that of passing it over land where growing vegetation could abstract the noxious material as plant food and elaborate it into something less injurious, leaving the watery residue to flow away through properly constructed channels or by seepage into the local river, and hence out to sea. This operation is known as " sewage irrigation ".

The good qualities of manure derived from human and farmyard waste had long been recognized. The present innovation lay in the application of very large quantities of sewage to extended areas, and in the fact that the primary object served was less that of obtaining abundant crops than the disposal of a community's sewage.

The earliest attempt of any magnitude of such disposal is connected with the Craigentinny Meadows,
developed out of part of a sandy waste between Edinburgh and the coast.  As early as 1734 the disposal of
part of the town sewage had resulted in some unsystematic reclamation, but by 1760 about 40 acres had been
laid out on the catch water system, the meadowland
increasing to more than eight times that amount during
the next hundred years.   When in full working order the
process was somewhat as follows :—The community
sewage of Edinburgh, after collection and standing for
settlement of the solid material, was led towards the
estuary of the Forth in a wide, open drain called the
" Foul Burn " ;  this burn was supplied with about
2,500,000 gallons of crude sewage every 24 hours during
the irrigating season, and from this burn the farmers
owning land along its course drew off their portion and
irrigated their territory, mainly on the catch water
plan.  Slopes were gentle, movement slow, and the
liquid lay on the ground in a sheet of about 4 inches in
thickness.  The land itself, once an ancient sea-beach,
sandy and very porous, allowed much of the liquid to
soak away underground, ultimately to reach the estuary,
which also received the remainder, after collection by
ditches or drains.  The moving water assisted aeration
of the ground, and brought the sewage food into close
contact with the plants, while the thinness of the sheet
prevented contamination of the stems.  The town corporation supplied the sewage liquid free, the farmer's
liability being a promise to use it at times and in quantities agreed upon.

About the middle of the nineteenth century, when this
form of irrigation was at the zenith of its utility, it
provided for some 323 acres divided among four or
five " farmers ".  The meadows then consisted of

the Craigentinny Meadows proper, covering about 220
acres, the Lochend Meadows, about 28 acres, the
Lochryn-on-Dalry Meadows, occupying about 40 acres,
and the Bridgend and Cairn Tows, totalling about
35 acres between them. Some of the land belonged
to the Earls of Haddington and Moray, and the rest
to private gentlemen-farmers. The Craigentinny and
Lochend Meadows produced between them about 200
acres of permanent pasture, and 50 acres of Italian rye-
grass. Three " watermen " were required for the
Craigentinny Meadows in summer and one in winter.
About 8 acres were good land, but too elevated to be
commanded by the feeding burn, and the sewage water
was lifted to them by steam pumps ; rye-grass was
grown here, receiving six to eight waterings a year.

It was not considered safe to pasture animals directly
upon these sewage meadows, and the grass produced was
cut for hay, or for feeding green. It was largely used
for the stall-feeding of dairy cows in the neighbouring
towns of Edinburgh, Leith, Musselburgh, and Portobello.
Each year at the beginning of April the season's grass
was sold by public roup or auction. It was bought as
it stood in the fields, in allotments of about an acre or
less, its new owners cutting and removing it at their
own cost. During the season, which ended in October,
about four cuts of permanent grass and five of rye-grass
were taken, the former aggregating 40 and the latter
60 tons to the acre. As a rule the sewage water was
turned on the ground for a day or two immediately after
each cut, and this, with the winter watering, meant
flooding ten or twelve times a year. By 1895 the cows
in Edinburgh and Leith were chiefly fed with this sewage
grass.

The Craigentinny method of sewage irrigation was for
some decades regarded as an example of " scientific

agriculture ", it being held that the milk yield was very much greater than that derived from consumption of an equal area of other grass. Its success led private individuals and public corporations to undertake similar ventures. Enterprising farmers in Cheshire and elsewhere were collecting the farmyard and domestic sewage, augmented by rain water and the run-off of heavy showers, storing it in suitable reservoirs, and distributing it over their fields, when dry, on the catch water principle. Sewage irrigation farms, fed by the sewage of neighbouring towns, villages and small groups of human population, soon sprang up all over the country. By 1877 some forty towns and a number of villages were getting rid of all or part of their sewage by this means, though the total amount of sewage irrigated land was only about 4,000 acres.

Except in the Craigentinny Meadows the sewage irrigation farms provided on occasion some actual grazing as well as cut forage, but Italian rye-grass remained the sewage crop *par excellence*. Some of the farms were private adventures merely obtaining free sewage from the town or village authorities ; some were Corporation farms, worked less for profit than for example and experimentation. The private ventures entailed rather more than a hundred owners and occupiers of land, of whom about sixty were tenant farmers with the right, but apparently not the desire, to refuse the use of sewage. About ¾ of the total farm owners or occupiers paid for the sewage either as out-fall rent, or increased land rent, or for the price of occasional dressings. At some of the farms the irrigation took place during the summer, except when the hay grass was tall or being made ; at others during both summer and winter ; at others more or less all the year round. This last was the case in the Plympton St. Mary (Plymouth) meadows, where the farmers were said to be " crazy after the sewage ".   Corporations such as Town Councils or Boards of Health had farms at Warwick, Banbury, Norwich, Bury St. Edmunds, Bedford, Croydon, and elsewhere.  The Warwick farm was hired and worked at a decided loss ;  the Croydon farm provided " sewage grass " for silage, and its irrigated fields made pastures for coach and draft horses of the City needing rest.

In England the sewage water was generally applied on the catch water system, though occasionally, as at Romford, the ridge and furrow method was adopted. The routine of the sewage irrigation farms was some-what as follows :  The ground was prepared to allow deep cultivation and provided when necessary with subsoil drains.   The sewage was poured on at the rate of about 400 tons per acre during a few hours, two such waterings being given during the growth of the crop, with an additional soaking after each cut.   The liquid lay about 4 inches deep.   Under proper conditions, 10–20 tons of succulent forage were obtained from about a month or five weeks' growth, and four or five cuts a year could be taken from approximately 3,000 to 12,000 tons of sewage.

The success of sewage irrigation farming depended largely upon the character of the soil and complete surface drainage of the water after use.  A porous, sandy soil was almost ideal ;  for with the heavier soil good artificial draining of the subsoil was an absolute necessity.  The " sewage " crops were varied, potatoes, cabbages, corn and other food crops for human con-sumption being grown in many places.   But there was a not unnatural prejudice against " human " food being grown under such conditions, hence the great prevalence of forage for cows and sheep.  This forage consisted mainly of Italian rye-grass, cut and fed green to tethered cows, meadow grass for hay, and some other feeding crops. Even here there was a feeling against using the milk produced by cows so fed, though the Medical Officer of Edinburgh, giving evidence before the River Pollution Commissioners in 1895, declared that he " had failed to detect any bad effect resulting from the use of such grass ".

The production of forage crops by sewage irrigation perhaps reached its zenith during the last decade of the nineteenth century. The method had some serious drawbacks which did not decrease with time. One such drawback was the frequent impossibility for a given venture to use its total allotment of sewage. The Craigentinny Meadows, for example, did not devour all the sewage coming their way, and much of the still-infected liquid passed into the Firth of Forth. A piece of land cannot deal with limitless sewage, and many farmers were dissatisfied because they were required to turn on the liquid in quantities beyond their need and at times when they did not want it. Some farmers disliked the idea of not being able to " take a few days off duty " when they wished, the Sewage Agreement entailing continuous and methodical work. Moreover, an increasing number of people were studying domestic hygiene, and believed that sewage so utilized was the cause of dire disease. Nor could men be forced by the authorities to start a sewage irrigation farm and the complete sewage of a community could rarely be disposed of in this manner.

Meanwhile the idea was gaining ground that sewage could be more cheaply disinfected by mechanical or even chemical means, and it at length became imperative to try some such means, since the irrigation method disposed of so little of the total community waste, even had the prejudice of this means of disposal not been increasing. To-day these means have been found, and the sewage irrigation farm has disappeared.

## CHAPTER XIII

THE AID OF APPLIED SCIENCE—3. AGRICULTURAL
CHEMISTRY

IT has been noted above how the revolution in agriculture and the invention of the Bramah Press
supplied the pastoral industry with new foods, whether
cultivated or "manufactured". By 1826 farmers were
experimenting in fattening their farm stock and publish-
ing their results when successful. In course of time the
enthusiasm so engendered became the inspiration of
much scientific investigation in the departments of pure
and applied chemistry attached to various agricultural
societies and colleges.

The pioneer in these researches was Sir Humphry
Davy, whose work bore upon the chemical composition
of the food required by animals and its relative proportions as supplied by natural and artificial forage.
Assuming that only substances soluble in water could be
nutritive to animals, Davy regarded fibre and fat as
entirely unnutritious, and starches, sugar and albumen
as all of equal food value. He also believed that
animals could extract the nutritive substances from
different kinds of food with equal ease. We know to-day
that none of these assumptions is true, but the interest
taken by so great a man stimulated others to further
investigation of the same food problems. Davy's
*Elements of Agricultural Chemistry*, the outcome of eight
lectures given by him in 1812 at the instigation of the
original Board of Agriculture, may be regarded as
having laid the foundations of agricultural chemistry.

About twenty-six years later the great German chemist Justus Liebig (1803–75), later created Baron von Liebig, came to the conclusion that animal fat is formed of carbohydrates (compounds composed of varying proportions of carbon, hydrogen and oxygen).

The investigation now ranged round the kinds of food that would give domestic animals the right amount of albumen and carbohydrate to produce the right amount and quality of meat and milk. The English chemists believed that the hay and roots fed to animals would vary with the farm, being governed by its customary routine and the quality of its agriculture. They therefore gave their attention chiefly to concentrates, as being richer in this or that chemical, and therefore capable of making good a recognized deficiency in the usual farm food. There were some experiments, however, upon the advantages of the different kinds of forage to be used in feeding different groups of animals otherwise living under similar conditions, according as they were being fed on larger or smaller quantities of roots or long fodder.

On the Continent the experiments were of the laboratory variety. Doctor Albert Thaer, physician of Celle, Hanover (b. 1752), worked upon the feeding value of foods, but believed that at least the fibre in mangolds had some nutritive value. His experiments were carried out upon working bullocks, and were based upon finding the weight of food necessary to keep them in good condition. He found that in feeding value 40 lb. of turnips were equal to 10 lb. of hay, etc. These investigations led eventually to the establishment of a unit, or norm, against which the value of the various foods could be assessed. Dr. Thaer was firmly convinced that farmers should be acquainted with the relative feeding values of food, so that they could make good deficiencies found existing in the customary diet. To disseminate his

ideas and to make further experiments he opened a
school which may be regarded as the first agricultural
school established in Germany.

Thaer's work was continued by Jean Baptiste
Boussingault (1802–77), Professor of Agricultural and
Analytical Chemistry at the Institute of Arts and Com-
merce, Paris. Boussingault came to the conclusion that
only the *woody* fibre in vegetables is indigestible to
animals. Unfortunately the badly planned experiments
of other investigators caused this line of practical
research to be suspended, and the work fell into the
hands of the laboratory men. Chemists and physiologists
turned their attention upon " food rations ", not in
terms of forage or concentrate, but in terms of chemical
compounds.

The work of Voit and Pettenkofer had shown that fat
is formed from albumen, and the chemists and physiologists were advising giving animals not so much hay,
or its equivalent, but so much albumen, sugar, and fat
per day, the proportion to be determined by the kind of
animal kept, its age, and the particular purpose for
which it was being reared. The reasoning was somewhat on these lines : the first food of all young animals
is milk, which contains much albumen ; therefore young
domestic animals must have much albumen ; and, as the
milk of cows contains much albumen, therefore albumen
is food. Later when experience and analysis showed that
clover, vetches, sainfoin, lucerne were not only superior
in food value to other forage, but contained more
albumen, it was argued that nitrogen was the most
essential element in foods, because albumen contains
much nitrogen. In this way food was reduced to its
chemical constituents, and the chemists began to issue
" norms " and constitute themselves the " stock-feeder's
advisers ". The method adopted was to get from

successful stock feeders the amounts and kinds of food given, analyse them for their proportions of albumen, fats, carbohydrates, and advise other stock feeders to feed with rations of similar chemical content.

In deciding upon the contents of a norm, there were not only errors of analysis, but no allowance was made for the power possessed by different species of animals to assimilate the food given them, which had been selected according to formula, and which contained a serious bias in favour of albumen, and it was as well that good farmers disregarded the rations of the theorists.

However, younger investigators, with some real farming experience, were coming to the fore and began to experiment upon more practical lines, " looking at the animal itself, rather than the test tube ". One of the earliest of these experimentalists to gain renown was Niels Johannes Fjord (d. 1889). He was the son of a schoolmaster and farmer of Jutland, and in 1858 became the first lecturer on Physics in the new Veterinary and Agricultural College at Copenhagen. Up to this point Danish farming was directed primarily to production of grain, dairy products and meat (bacon and sometimes beef) holding the second place. The cows and young stock were fed on the summer pastures. As grain prices fell the crops were reduced and more attention was devoted to dairying. The milk separator came into use, roots increased, cows were made more productive, butter made all the year round, more liquid food produced, more pigs and calves reared. Between 1858 and 1871 Fjord invented a number of dairy implements to increase the standard of the produce, and carried out great reforms in the dairy farming industry with the co-operation of farmers, dairy managers, and specially trained assistants. The Farmers' Society, the College, private funds and later the State contributed to pay the expenses of his experiments.  Among other things, Fjord proved that mangolds are more nutritious than turnips.

After his death his successors in Denmark and Sweden turned their attention to concentrates as factors in better beef production, and experiments on mutton production were carried out concurrently on British farms, but were less conclusive, the habits and more open life of the sheep making it less easy to check the quality and quantity of the food eaten.

The outcome of over a century of experimentation may be summed up briefly thus :  foods contain water, mineral salts, albumen (found in white of egg, muscles of animals), and other proteins, fats, and carbohydrates (sugar, starch, fibrous parts of plants).  Animal rations should contain all these ingredients, but the breeder needs to know the minimum of albumen required, which varies with the species, age, purpose for which the animal is fed, the amount of ingredients producing energy and fat (explained in terms of starch and called the " starch equivalent "), the proportions of each ingredient which are digested or ejected, and the capacity of each animal to deal with larger or smaller amounts of long fodder, roots, concentrates, etc.

Attention was early drawn to the *mineral* content of food, and in 1859 Grouven, the maker of the first widely recognized norm, suggested that the rations should contain appropriate minerals.  Fifteen years later Wolff enumerated the kinds and quantities of minerals in lean and fat cattle, sheep, and pigs.  Subsequent work has shown that, as a last analysis, animals obtain their minerals from the soil.   Many pastures are deficient in phosphates, and when they carry breeding or young stock the phosphates originally present in a pasture tend to become exhausted.  This is because large quantities of phosphates (and lime too for that matter) are required for building up the bones and flesh of the growing animal. It is therefore essential in the case of many pastures carrying such stock to work in a supply of phosphate. Many kinds of cattle pastures are likely to be deficient in chlorine, a deficiency that may be made good with a salt lick. Pastures without clovers are short of lime. For maximum growth sheep need proportionately less chlorine but more lime than do cattle, a need reflected in the basal crops of the Norfolk four-course rotation, red clover, an excellent lime-carrying plant, and in the practice of putting young lambs off the hill on a clover aftermath or pasture wherever possible. Lime-containing concentrates (concentrates containing peas, beans, or linseed cake) are fed to sheep in greater proportion than to cattle. Before calving, a dry cow needs concentrates and a full supply of added minerals, if she is being fed on long fodder alone or with roots, but if she have a clover pasture a salt lick will suffice.

It was early recognized that growing plants took " goodness " from the ground ; it was even recognized that a soil might be deficient in an element necessary to plant growth, and attempts were made to restore fertility and supply this lack by means of manure.

The earliest manure used in agricultural operations was farmyard manure, one of its good qualities being that its application diminishes the tenacity of a heavy soil and the porosity of a light one. The liquid ingredient is very useful on sandy soils, but not on clay. Its effect on grass and root crops is rapid. To prevent waste, straw and other litter are laid down to absorb the animal refuse, and of course they add to the manurial value on their own account. But farmyard manure is bulky and expensive to handle when required for large areas ; it is liable to waste and its solid ingredients give rather slow results. Its true worth depends on the animal supplying it, and the care, attention and food that animal has received. It is rich in nitrogen. In the manor system the planting out of the farmyard manure was part of the routine, but additional nitrogen was gained for the soil by digging in wool clippings, the parings of horses' hoofs, dried blood, etc. To obtain manure some open-field farmers summered sheep, from Bagshot Heath for example, for folding at night on their arable fallow from April to October. Cottars with only common rights drove their sheep from one open field to another, receiving 1s. per week per score or some winter grazing on the commons for this boon to the arable fallow.

In the first half of the nineteenth century chemical manures began to make their appearance. In 1830 nitrate of soda was first brought from Chile, and ten years later Peruvian guano, the droppings of birds upon some of the islands of Peru, came to be used as a soil manure. These nitrates gave such marvellous results that nitrogen was presently regarded as the most essential part of the manure. The need for other ingredients was also recognized, and bones were crushed with a hammer and " dug in ", though after 1840 iron rollers worked by steam power effected a more scientific pulverization.

In 1840 Liebig published his work tracing the connection between the nutrition of plants and the composition of the soil. This book was at once translated into English under the title of *Agricultural Chemistry*, and in it he described how the phosphates in bones could be made soluble by treatment with sulphuric acid. In England Liebig's work was taken up by John Bennet Lawes (later Sir John B. Lawes, Bart.), who experimented with the action of sulphuric acid on bone ash, coprolites, and mineral or rock phosphates, thus obtaining a superphosphate which could be used as manure. To-day all superphosphate is made from mineral phosphates, while long ago coprolites ceased to have any commercial importance. The action of Lawes' superphosphate was tried in small-scale experiments during 1837–9, and on field crops 1840–1. Two years later Lawes turned his farm into an Experimental Station to be famous as the Rothamsted Experimental Station. He was assisted by Dr. Joseph Henry Gilbert, later Sir Henry Gilbert, and soon secured the attention of the National Agricultural Societies of England and Scotland, which gave prominence to the Rothamsted work in their annual publications.

In 1843 Lawes began the manufacture of super-phosphates at Deptford, and showed how great was the value of ammonium salts (obtained from the by-products of gas-making) as a fertilizer for farm crops.

It is now recognized that nitrogen, phosphates, potash, lime in assimilable form are of the greatest value to land as chemical manures. Another source of manurial nitrogen is calcium cyanamide, obtained from electric works. Fish and meat guano are misnomers, but useful, and a top dressing of seaweed is sometimes given to grassland. Under the present system of farming nitrogen is often returned to the soil by the deliberate planting of clover and other leguminous crops, though it is uncertain how far plants can obtain and make use of the small amount of nitrogen so given. The ploughing in of mustard, buckwheat, and rape improves the soil rather than returns nitrogen to it.

In grassland and sheep husbandry the use of super-phosphates as manure is now supplanted by the use of basic slag, obtained as a refuse in the manufacture of steel by the Thomas-Gilchrist process. Mineral phosphates are also used upon certain pastures to a fair extent. Potash for use as a fertilizer was formerly obtained from wood ashes, but since 1861 it has been obtained from the Stassfurt and later the Alsace mines, where it is found in the form of the mineral kainite. Salt liberates the potash in the soil. Lime ameliorates the texture of heavy soils and is a direct plant food; moreover, when given to a soil hitherto deficient or without it, lime causes the growth of a more nutritious type of herbage. The practice of marling was once a well-recognized aid to agriculture, though it has now disappeared from Norfolk, where it was so successfully advocated by Townshend. In Kent broken-up chalk is often dug into the soil of the London clay, and possibly this variation of marling was that in vogue long ago by the Neolithic agriculturalists of these regions, but chalking has been and is still the practice wherever chalk is overlaid by not too deep deposits of clay. Soot and sewage sludge are occasionally used as fertilizers.

The above account by no means exhausts the number or the utility of the artificial manures.

## CHAPTER XIV

## CROSS BREDS : SHEEP

*" The Mountain Sheep are sweeter; but the Valley Sheep are
fatter "*

THE early successes of Bakewell, Ellman, and others
stimulated livestock breeders with the necessary
capital to experiment on local sheep in order to obtain
better wool and meat in return for their increased outlay
in forage and pasture. Moreover, the change in some
districts due to agricultural progress made it necessary
to improve and replace local breeds where adaptation to
the new conditions was not possible.

The experiments usually began by engrafting new
blood upon some native breed whose main qualities
peculiarly fitted it for the environment in which it had
long been established ; in this way useful but fading
strains were revived, or some new quality was ingrained
which enhanced its commercial value. When the desired
type was obtained after experimentation over a longer
or shorter period, the type was perpetuated by interbreeding among the progeny of the cross, such animals
as showed undesirable characteristics being at once
eliminated from the stock. On occasion, however,
native blood has not supplied a conspicuous element in
the cross bred destined for a particular locality.

Nomenclature is not always consistent, partly through
ignorance and partly through a traditional bias in favour
of some particular term ; this being understood, the
classification adopted below will probably suffice to keep
matters clear.

The immediate descendants of the first matings
between two different breeds are the *cross breds*, and
they can be further differentiated as the " improved
native breeds ", when the amount of alien blood has
been small in comparison with the native strain ; the
true " cross breds " where the two strains have been
more equally mingled, a permanent but distinctive type
having been produced that possesses in no small degree
qualities arising from both strains ; and " half breds ",
where the cross of the first generation is the object,
mating beyond the first cross being common only among
a limited number of breeds, such as, for example, the
second crosses between mountain or hill half-bred ewes
and Border Leicester, Suffolk, or Oxford Down rams.
We shall see later that the object to be obtained is the
production of fat lamb.

From the commercial standpoint the object of the
crossing is the production of better wool,[1] better meat,
more " mutton " sheep, earlier and better lamb, and
better eating of the regional resources of forage or grass ;
the superior vigour, hardiness, and fertility (the latter a
possible consequence of the capacity for early fattening)
possessed by the cross bred when compared with the
pure bred parent strains, are also qualities of value.

There were probably few types of sheep existing in
Pre-Roman and Roman Britain, but long continuance
in their respective habitats brought about some
differentiation of these types ; it is also possible that
the primitive sheep, like the primitive Britons, were
ousted by invaders from the plains and took refuge in

---

[1] *Long wools* : Staple 10–16 inches, wavy, lustrous, Lincoln,
Leicester, Border Leicester, Cotswold, Romney Marsh, Devon,
Scotch Blackface. *Medium wools* : semi-lustrous, Cheviot,
Oxford Down, Suffolk, Welsh Mountain. *Short wools* : staple
4–6 inches, crimpy, Southdown, Shropshire, Hampshire. The
distinction is often only between long and short wools.

the less accessible highlands of the north and west.   It is in these regions that their descendants are to be found to-day.

Perhaps the most useful classification of the sheep of Great Britain is according to their habitat, for habitat plays a great part in the development of their wool and meat and other qualities.   These habitats may be broadly distinguished as lowlands, heaths and downs, hills and mountains.

The lowland sheep inhabit for the most part the rich grassy lowlands of our Midlands and coastal lands, especially where there are well-drained marshes.   A characteristic feature of such sheep is their long, some-what coarse, wool.   They were the domestic sheep of the Midlands in earlier times, when wool was greatly desired for the family loom.   The meat of these " long-wools ", especially in the old, unimproved state, was coarse and fat in comparison with that of Down sheep, but the great weight of the fleece and its lustrous quality were decided assets.   The wool was combed and spun by the worsted process.

The heath breeds occupy sandy heaths and down-lands.   In the first case they are sometimes called " forest breeds ", the true meaning of forest being an open woodland, or, like the Scotch " deer forests ", even territory with almost an entire absence of trees.   These breeds give a short fine wool and excellent mutton. Some of them have spread into the hill country in the north, where climate has caused the development of a longer fleece, and the mutton has deteriorated a little in consequence.   The fine quality of the short wool of the Southdown is surpassed only by the merino ; this wool, once the chief source of the fine woollen trade, is still used for flannels and hosiery yarn.   The Down breeds are also breeds par excellence for arable land.

The mountain breeds are sheep of the high hills, with short, often very fine wool, giving a good protection in rough weather.   The fleeces are variable, the roughest wool being used for carpets and tweeds, and the fine Cheviot wool, for example, for woollens, while the soft short wool of the Welsh mountain sheep is also excellent for flannels.   The mountain breeds more nearly represent the ancient sheep than do the others.   They are less altered from the old, antique type, but the special qualities of the habitats have brought about differences, and some are more carefully bred in one district than another.   The  " unimproved "  mountain breeds are very useful where herbage provides but meagre fare. The Scotch Blackface, once a heath breed, but now inhabiting the heather-clad mountains of Scotland and England from Caithness to the moorlands of Derbyshire and Staffordshire, occupy a greater area than any other sheep bred in the British Isles.   These Blackfaces will find food in situations where the Welsh mountain sheep would find it impossible to secure a living.   The mutton of these mountain breeds is excellent, but in some of them the development of a hairy (kempy) quality in the wool reduces the value for textile manufacture.   In general, mountain sheep are too agile to be kept upon culti-vated or enclosed ground unless special precautions are taken.

The primitive sheep of Britain were probably poly-cerate, as many as four horns being found upon some of their modern descendants.   As existing at present the primitive breeds have usually, though not always, been improved by a dash of alien blood or better feeding. Among the most ancient and least altered survivals are the sheep of our northern islands, Man, Hebrides, Shetlands.

The Manx breeds of sheep are both horned and polled,

white of colour except in the case of the Loughtin or
Loughtan sheep, which are brown, and the Keeir sheep,
which are black. The old Loughtan nearly became
extinct owing to the great number of larger sheep
brought into the Island by Scotchmen who rented the
Manx commons. Later a determined and successful
effort was made to revive this ancient breed, which is
hardy, picturesque, gives good wool and excellent
mutton, casts its fleece in summer, and possesses the
short tail which seems characteristic of some of the
denizens of Man.

The unimproved Shetland sheep are strange, goat-like
animals, which may be white, black, tan, brown (moorit),
or the mixed grey known as *sheila*. The sheep are small
and the lambs so tiny that they can take shelter from the
cold wind in rabbit burrows. In spite of the introduction
of newer breeds the Shetlands hold their own in their
native haunts, their long silky fleeces, soft as down, and
their power of fending for themselves, peculiarly fitting
them for life in a perpetually moist climate and upon
undrained pasture. The greater part of the interior
of the country is rough, undivided " scathold " over
which the sheep roam at large, and without any special
shelter. The Shetland sheep come into contact with
man only at the lambing season, or where they are
collected for sale, or in July for the " ruing ", when the
wool is pulled off the sheep's back, the old wool being
long and the new too short to be plucked. This " ruing "
leaves the animal with a coat to protect it against
inclement weather. If the wool is not pulled off by hand,
it is cast later, as with the Manx breeds.

The Shetland sheep and similar native sheep of the
Orkneys possess a curious " water " sense : twice a day
as the tide ebbs they crowd to the shore and browse
upon the seaweed. In winter seaweed makes up a large

part of their food, the animals swallowing long strands
of it " like men swallowing their own beards ".[1]

Beyond domestic use the commercial value of the
Shetland sheep is in the wool, used for shawls, jumpers,
berets, stockings, three-piece suits and other articles of
wear which the women knit not only in their homes but
when taking their walks abroad.   The shawls have a
wide renown, and there is afoot at this moment a very
determined effort to find an English market for Shetland
home industries of woollen glove making, sports coats,
etc., and in cured sheep skins.   With a view to improving
the mutton other sheep have been introduced both here
and in the Orkneys, the Scotch Blackface, the Cheviot,
and the Border Leicester being the chief.   In the Shetlands the new-comers number less than half the total
sheep census, but in the less inclement Orkneys they
hold a much greater position.

Among the ancient breeds still inhabiting our
mountain districts may be mentioned the Herdwick,
the Scotch Blackface, the Cheviot, the Lonk, the
Derbyshire Grit, and the four main breeds of Wales.

The origin of the Herdwick sheep of our Lake District
is a matter of dispute.   A popular but unreliable legend
makes them descend from a flock of some 40 sheep cast
on the Cumberland coast from the wreck of a Spanish
galleon in 1588, though the wreck has also been dated
the eighteenth century.   Another tradition ascribes
their introduction to the Norsemen, and Herdwicks are
mentioned in the twelfth-century records of Furness
Abbey and its dependent sheep farms.

The origin of the Scotch Blackfaces is equally obscure.
Their presence in our Island has also been associated
with the Spanish Armada, while another tradition gives
James IV the honour of its original introduction from a

[1] The Rev. R. Logan Mitchell, Lerwick.

foreign breed into Ettrick Forest. A more probable tradition connects it with the ancient " Dunfaces " which were kept near every homestead on the lower hills when the mountains were over-run by wolves and foxes. In the course of the eighteenth century agriculture pushed upwards, taming the wild and making the mountain slopes safe for sheep, especially in Lanarkshire, the head-quarters of the Blackfaces, where a change in the method of sheep-rearing brought a change in the colour of the face. The great value of the Blackfaces caused the zeal for improvement to spread northward, so that, except in the Orkneys and Shetlands, not many specimens of the earlier " Dunfaces " remain.

The Cheviot sheep received their present name in 1791 from Sir John Sinclair. The rising wool prices at the beginning of the next century helped the Cheviot to oust the Blackface from a great part of the Border, but owing to the severe winter of 1860 the hardier and larger breed regained its former habitat and the Cheviots, greatly reduced in numbers, were once more restricted to their own hills. The return of the Blackfaces was assisted by a fall in the price of wool and the greater demand for tasty mutton. The Cheviots have now wandered widely, and have been introduced with great success into Caithness and Sutherland.

The Lonk is a hardy sheep of the wet hills and moors of Lancashire (said to have been known formerly as Loncashire). Its habitat is rough grass and heather pasture, and hence its spreading into the Yorkshire Fells and mountain country of north-west Derbyshire is not surprising. The Lonk is a horned sheep, with a black and white face, with a curly, heavy, long, close, but coarse woolled fleece, well adapted to protect it in its misty home. Like the Lonk, the Swaledale and Penistone are rough fell native sheep of long ancestry derived

from  the  same  general  blackface  mountain  stock,  inhabiting the moors and hills of parts of Westmorland and
north-west  Yorkshire.

The  Derbyshire  Gritstone  (or  Dale-o'-Goyt) is  a  hornless heath sheep native to the hills and dales of the Peak
District

The Welsh sheep represent a very old breed native to
the highest hills of Wales.   The advance of agriculture
has curtailed their range to the poorer soils of the Welsh
Highlands, and they are found on the gorse and heather
lands and attached to the cottages of the hill folk.   The
males are always, the females occasionally horned, and
faces may be white, rusty brown, speckled or grey.   As
with  all  mountain  breeds,  the  ewes  are  good  nurses.
The fine wool is sometimes kempy when the pasturage is
exceptionally  bleak.   Among  existing  ancient  breeds
are the Clun Forest, Kerry Hill, Plinlimmon, Radnor,
and Ryeland, all of which have undergone some slight
improvement.   They  are  reared  among  the  roughest
conditions of the uplands, subsisting on the hardest fare.
The ewes are very active and when taken to the lowlands
require  enclosures  with  high  fences.   The  sheep  are
horned, have white, black or tan faces, and the fleeces
give  a  soft  " flannel "  wool.

The Clun Forest sheep, indigenous to the south-west
corner of Shropshire, and the Kerry Hill sheep, named
after  the  parish  of  Kerry  in  Montgomeryshire,  have
probably benefited by crossing in the one case with the old
Ryeland, which long existed on the richest lands about
Clun Forest, and in the other with the Shropshire sheep.
The result is that, though primarily a forest sheep, they
will feed on the hills in summer and can winter on roots.
The meat is first class, but the wet air makes the wool
a little kempy ;  since they do so well on heavy and wet
grazings, they are to be found on the Sussex Weald.

L

The Radnors are the sheep of the counties of Breck-nock (Brecon Hill), Montgomery and some part of Merioneth and Radnor. They spend their summer on the wild open mountain heath, but if the winter be severe the ewes and young sheep are brought down to enclosed lands. They are less improved than the other two forest breeds, but the ewes are sold at the fairs of Kington, Knighton and Builth for crossing in the adjoining English counties with Shropshire, Lincoln, and Cotswold sheep.

The Plinlimmon is an ancient Welsh breed, very rare. The present Ryeland has been produced by the improve-ment of an old breed through Leicester blood. About 100 years ago the Ryelands of Hereford occupied poor forest land south of the River Wye, formerly much cultivated for *rye*, hence the name of the breed. The sheep are white-faced, hornless, hardy and give both fine wool and good mutton. They are believed to have some merino blood.

Other native heath or forest strains are the Cannock Chase (Staffordshire), Longmynd and Morfe Common sheep (Shropshire), all black-faced and horned.

The native heath breeds of Dartmoor and Exmoor are of very ancient lineage. They have been improved with some Leicester blood,[1] though the Exmoor has also a Cheviot strain. The Dartmoor sheep is rather larger in body than the general run of mountain sheep : it provides rich mutton which is finished off for the butcher in the lowlands. The Exmoor, or Porlock, breed is smaller, and native to the uncultivated heaths and commons of west Somerset and north Devon. A very hardy sheep, it is one of the best to place on poor natural pastures, and hence is found far beyond its native home.

[1] Henceforward, unless actually stated, " Leicester " signifies the " new " or " Bakewell " Leicester breed.

Burial in a snowdrift for several days fails to kill this sheep. It can be folded on roots, and draft ewes sent to the lowlands will winter on rough grass and clear up the fields already " eaten over " by more fastidious sheep.

Among the native Down Breeds the Southdown takes a pre-eminent place. It is, of course, in no sense a cross bred, but it can cross very successfully with other heath breeds, imparting to them its valuable qualities of early maturity, good mutton, fat lambs, and arable folding. These crosses are known as the Down Breeds— the Shropshire, Hampshire, Oxford, Suffolk, etc. ; in some form or other Southdown blood has influenced all our present middle and short woolled sheep.

Another native Down Breed is one named the Old Wiltshire, Hampshire or Berkshire, according to locality. Like the Southdown, the Old Wiltshire Horn was folded on arable at nights and travelled several miles a day to feed on the grassy Downs. This sheep has been extinct in its native quarters since 1819, but some remnants of the breed are still to be found in Wales. In the days when Welsh dealers collected sheep from the English Midlands and southern counties for removal to Wales, the Old Wiltshire Horn made part of the stock. In this way " Welsh Wiltshires " escaped the Southdown crossing which brought about their extinction in their native home, and have been kept true to type by selection. A large, imposing, white-faced sheep, it was not a mutton breed and was kept primarily for the wool and dung. The Old Berkshires were very similar to the old Wilt-shires, as is also the Dorset Horn, the oldest and best of the upland horned breeds.

Records of 1793 hint that this last-named sheep underwent an early crossing with the older Southdown, Hampshire, Wiltshire or Somerset sheep, but the

Dorset Horn existed practically unimproved till 1817, when the breeders took it in hand. About 1886 the great improvement in size, weight of wool—which is fine and of medium staple—and the early maturity of the lamb came to be recognized. The change was largely due to a turnip, corn, and cake feed, and careful breeding among the Dorset Horns (or " Horns " simply in Dorset) possessing the required qualities. The horns of the rams are large and curved, and are hung up in halls as ornaments. The sheep accommodate themselves to many lairs ; they have long been kept in Purbeck flourishing alike on kimmeridge clay, chalk, and oolite soils. They extend also into Somerset and the Isle of Wight. They are adapted for high feeding on arable farms, and the sheep are sold at the Dorchester July and September fairs.

The Dorset Horn had a long struggle for supremacy with the Southdown. The " Horns " gave more wool per sheep, but the Southdowns were better fitted to crop the close herbage of the chalklands, and being smaller, more could feed per acre ; also their wool was the more profitable at a time when wool was a great commercial asset. Ultimately the Dorset Horns were driven from the chalk to better land in the western part of their county, where oolite, lower greensand, etc., gave a tolerably fertile soil for the arable feed when the sheep were folded on green or root crops at night, and moderately good upland pasture for the day. The ewes often give two crops of lambs a year.

The Dorset Down sheep originated from the parent West Country stock. They are popular with Dorset farmers because they do well when hurdled on arable with grazing on the pastures after the usual Down breed custom. Their mutton is excellent.

The native longwools are grazing sheep of the lowlands or low hills ; the Leicester, perhaps the most famous of these breeds, is not to be regarded as a cross bred.  Leicesters have been used, however, to improve another famous native sheep—the Cotswolds.

These latter sheep are native to the Cotswold Hills in Gloucester, and as " wold " in the Saxon tongue signified a treeless hill, and " cotes " the low sheds in which the sheep took refuge during the winter cold, it is held that these wolds of the sheep cotes were named from the circumstance of their sheep husbandry.  The Cotswold Hills are of oolitic formation, the soil being of a reddish loam, not very fertile, but rich in lime, and producing a short sweet grass upon which long-woolled sheep have been kept certainly since Roman times.  There is no reason to suppose that they were not here previously, though a well-known writer upon agriculture has said, rather unkindly, that the sheep are too stupid to have been on these hills prior to the Roman introduction of some cultivation, for they would have been destroyed by the wild beasts.

The improvement of the ancient breed was effected at the end of the eighteenth and beginning of the nineteenth century.  It was necessitated by the commercial demand for a finer wool than that given by the old Cotswolds, and the change was the more easily effected because the land was being steadily enclosed for agriculture, increasing the resources of an arable feed.  The method followed the customary lines,—some crossing with Bakewell's improved Leicesters, followed by careful selection and management.  Cotswold wool, long, lustrous, coarse, still sells well, but the mutton is decidedly second class.

The Cotswold sheep are now chiefly arable, but the good constitution ingrained in the breed by their earlier hardships enables the Cotswold blood to provide good crosses for poor land and a wet winter lair ; such lairs, in fact, suit them better than more prosperous conditions.

The Leicester sheep, whose "improvement" has already been discussed, have played so large a part in the improvement of breeds, that a few words upon their subsequent history may not be out of place. When moved from their native district they do better in the cross than when pure, and better in the north than in the south. When wool commanded a good price, the Leicester wool, even where "improved", sold for less than other long wools, so that the flocks decreased in the home district, but increased further north, where the growing industrial population of that time preferred rather than disdained the overmuch fat in the Leicester mutton. The sheep are, however, a little lacking in stamina. In 1890, when the Leicester breed seemed likely to die out, the Leicester Sheep Breeders' Association was formed, and built up an improved sheep with a stronger constitution. It is still a sheep of early maturity and puts on flesh. Though primarily a grass sheep, for more than a century it has also been reared pure and in cross for feeding on roots, an expensive keep not justified by the over-fat and flavourless meat. The Leicesters may be found on the upland soils of north Derbyshire, where they are called "limestones". The Bakewell Leicester still holds its ground in the Midlands, and especially in the East and North Ridings of Yorkshire, where it is the more common sheep. Leicesters will make more mutton from a given quantity of food than any other breed.

The old Lincoln sheep inhabited the rich pastures of the Lincoln Fens long before Bakewell's time. Long-woolled, ungainly, white-faced, the heaviest of all our sheep, the old Lincoln was renowned for its great weight of fleece, and so was bred for its wool. At certain periods of the year the ewes made use of the wolds and heaths of Lincolnshire, exercising a transhumance recalling that of the ancient Southdowns. The improve-

ment was effected between 1740 and 1755 by the introduction of Leicester blood through rams of the Bakewell
stock. The result was a " new " Lincoln of earlier
maturity, better form, greater aptitude to put on flesh,
and better mutton. The excellent wool qualities of the
old breed,—strong, highly lustrous,—were maintained.
Being a heavy feeder the Lincoln is in limited request,
and is mainly found in its native and adjacent counties.

The improved Lincoln is wonderfully prolific, two,
three, and even four lambs being dropped at a birth.
Hardy and healthy, its resemblance to the Kent or
Romney sheep makes it probable that both breeds
have a common origin in the white-faced Flanders
sheep.

The Wensleydale or Yorkshire Leicester is another
interesting breed derived from a Leicester cross with the
native Yorkshire or old Teeswater sheep, a breed possibly
allied to the old Lincolns. About 130 or so years ago
this sheep was accounted the largest sheep in Britain,
and was bred for its size, its long wool being scanty.
The crossing represents a gradual development over a
long period rather than attempts to attain some specific
ideal. The immense sheep were taken in hand by Culley,
the brothers Collings, and Christopher Mason, who tried,
without success, to get an improved cross with the
Lincoln. The Dishley Leicester gave better results, the
size being reduced and the wool increased (1825–35).
After 1810 there were few Old Teeswaters left though the
new type was by no means fixed. In 1841 Blue Cap,
a two-shear ram from a Teeswater ewe and a Leicester
ram, was shown at the meeting of the Royal Agricultural
Society, then taking place at Liverpool. After its return
home it was used on Teeswater ewes for the next eight
years or so. Besides his blue head, Blue Cap was
symmetrical, robust, and excelled in both quality and

quantity of wool, merits which were passed on to his
numerous descendants.   The wide diffusion of Blue Cap
blood through the dale eventually fixed the type, since
few other out-crosses were tried.   The name Wensleydale Longwool was given in 1876.   The breed is a hardy
one, an excellent sheep for the moors, not needing to
come to the homestead except for lambing.   It is the
sheep of the tenant farmer, and the flocks are small.
The wool is an asset, giving a pure lustre of the finest
class, silky and of long staple.   The sheep is peculiarly
adapted for crossing, imparting its good qualities to the
cross.   The most usual crosses are with the Lonk, the
Herdwick, the Cheviot, and the Scotch Blackface, so
that numbers of " Wensleydales " are sent yearly into
Scotland.   As an improved Teesdale the sheep is a
popular long-woolled breed in Northumberland.   The
high-class long wool and the large proportion of lean
mutton make a unique combination.

Other ancient " improved " longwool sheep are the
Devon Longwool of Devon and Somerset, and the
Southam of South Devon and Cornwall.

The present Devon Longwool has been derived from
grafting the Leicester upon local types—the Bampton
and Southam Notts.   Some Lincoln blood may have
been infused subsequently.   The Devon Longwool is
more valuable than either of the original Notts, being
better shaped, smaller boned, and of earlier maturity.
It is also more productive in meat and wool than the
Leicester.   It will thrive on hard and high land, and is
never housed.   It is very useful on the Somerset
Marshes.

The South Devon, a sheep with curly, dense, long and
lustrous wool, represents the Southam Notts improved
by the new Leicester.   It thrives on the rich lowland or
marsh pasture of South Devon, can be reared on grass or

in fold, and maintains its good condition under hard fare and exposure to inclement weather. It is vigorous and thrifty, a sheep of big weight and early maturity.

The last of the grazing longwool sheep we shall consider are the Kent or Romney Marsh sheep. The old type, settled on the marshes from time immemorial, was a loose-jointed, big-bellied sheep, with long, coarse wool and described by Cobbet as being " white as a piece of writing paper ". The winter keep on the Marsh must always have provided poor fare, and even in early times the uplands of Surrey and Sussex gave hospitality to all but the oldest ewes at that season. The hardy constitution of the Romney Marsh sheep has been built up on a varied keep, diversity of habitat, and inclement weather conditions. The earlier improvements were effected through Leicester rams, but too much crossing with this sheep of a more propitious native environment seemed at one time likely to end in disaster and crossing had to be suspended. A chance infusion of Cheviot blood has greatly improved the quality of the mutton, which now ranks first among the muttons of the coarse, long-woolled British sheep. It is said that Cheviot sheep brought in pre-railway days by water for sale in London, were landed on the Kentish coast and when a glut in the market or trade depression reduced the price, so that turnpike tolls and market dues were likely to swallow up the profits, the dealers preferred to sell them to the upland farmers, and in consequence, they mated " promiscuously " with some of the agisted Romney Marsh sheep—to the benefit of the mutton !

The above account more or less exhausts the lists of ancient breeds, revivified, or improved, but not fundamentally changed. We have now to consider the true cross breds, which are less " improved natives " than practically new types, capable of handing on intact the qualities of the cross bred without further recourse to either of the component breeds.

The Border Leicester, which represents one of the earlier of these crosses, has already been considered.

We shall begin with the cross breds based on the short-woolled Southdowns, of which the " new Hampshire " is perhaps the earliest example.  This breed was constructed out of the old West Country sheep of the South Downs, once bred on the chalks of Berkshire, Hampshire, Wiltshire, and Dorsetshire, and even in Sussex and Surrey.  Of these the Berkshire Nott, sometimes horned and sometimes polled, was a large, strong, active sheep, good in the fold but slow in fattening, and giving much wool.  The old Hampshire and Wiltshire were very much alike, and have been already considered.

Early in the nineteenth century the improved Southdown was introduced into Hampshire and Wiltshire, and might eventually have ousted the native breeds. But about 1817, when enclosure was going on rapidly, large areas of pasture serving the Southdown sheep were broken up and put to arable, to be additionally fertilized later by the use of artificial manure.  This arable farming was expensive, but as it provided forage crops and roughage in the shape of aftermaths, farmers and breeders wished to adapt their pastoral farming to meet this expense.  Assets of the native breeds were hardiness, early maturity, and large size, giving large joints for the large feeding now made possible by the new agriculture.  The Hampshire wether lambs could be ready for sale in late summer or early autumn, whereas the smaller Southdown had to be kept much longer in order to obtain joints of saleable size.  The farmers and breeders therefore determined to secure a sheep giving good young or youngish meat, and of greater size, and this was done by crossing the Southdowns with the

Hampshires.   The leading breeding experiments were carried out by Mr. Humphrey of Oak Ash, near Wantage, and Mr. James Rawlence of Bulbridge, the one mating the best old Hampshire Down ewes with Southdown rams of the Jonas Webb flock (up to 1868), and the other mating Southdown ewes with Hampshire rams.   The result was the modern Hampshire, a sheep of large size, rapid growth, and early maturity, the wether producing large joints of good-tasting mutton, while the ewes can winter cheaply on roughage.   In this new Hampshire, the old Wiltshire, Hampshire, and Berkshire Nott ancestry accounts for the large size, and the Southdown strain for the quality of the wool and mutton.   It is a breed of the chalk and chalky lands with arable near by, the sheep living close folded on forage crops in summer, turnips in winter, with additional cake and dry food. The grassy Downs provide daytime pastures.

One of the most useful sheep of the cross breds is the Shropshire.   This breed was built up early in the nineteenth century from the indigenous sheep of Long Mynd, Cannock Chase, and Morfe Common round Shrewsbury.   Enclosure and the increasing arable cultivation had made it locally desirable to have a sheep with folding and forage propensities.   The method employed involved an early infusion of Leicester and Cotswold blood into the native stock, and subsequently much more extensive crossing with the Southdown.   In its home region the breed enjoys both hill pastures and cultivated fields, while its origin has made it adaptable to great variety of soil and climate, and it is bred in both Scotland and Ireland.   The Shropshire is a hardy, handsome, docile sheep, with high-grade mutton and wool, which its great size causes to exceed in weight both the mutton and wool of the Southdown sheep.

Another useful cross bred has been the Oxford Down,

the latest, largest, and finest-looking of the Down breeds. The oolite measures of the Gloucester Cotswolds spread through Oxfordshire to Northamptonshire, providing a sticky yellow soil resting on porous limestone, so that, as with chalk soils, the surface is dry in spring. Thus the hill pastures give " limestone " grass, and near by is a fairly fertile soil for forage crops ; in winter there is much mud and wet. Here is the original home of the Cotswold sheep, which can retain their good qualities under such adverse conditions as those of a winter spent in the cold wet folds of the arable oolites.

About 1827 wealthy sheepowners [1] began to experiment with the Cotswold sheep as basis in producing a new breed of sheep which should have a weight of wool equal to that of the longwool sheep, but of Down quality. The crossing was between Cotswold rams and Hampshire ewes, some Southdown blood most probably also taking part. The breed was recognized about 1840, and nineteen years later received its name of Oxford Down from the region of its installation.

The Oxford Downs give lambs well suited for the early fat lamb trade. Owing to their hardiness shearlings and rams in large numbers are sent annually to Scotland. They are crossed on longwools for maintaining or increasing size, and giving Down quality to the mutton. In Scotland they are crossed with the Blackface, Cheviot, and Border Leicester for lamb, and when it is desirable to have smaller meat, with the Southdown.

The last of the down sheep is the Suffolk, a sheep of Suffolk, Cambridge, and Essex. At the beginning of the nineteenth century there was an active, hardy, horned breed of superior mutton known as the Norfolk upon which the Southdown was extensively used for improving its form and fattening properties, and in 1886 the

[1] Especially Mr. John Twynam of Whitchurch, Hants.

Southdown-Norfolk cross was officially recognized as the Suffolk.   The horn has gone but the high quality of the mutton remains.   The breed is prolific, hardy, active, the least liable to foot-rot of any Down breed.   Though better suited to dry lair and dry climate, it has been taken to Scotland.   A grass and arable sheep, a sheep of poor heath or rich marshes, it gives good crosses with the Cheviot.

We have now to consider the half breds or cross breds of the first generation.   These half breds are raised for some special purpose, and generally speaking the two partners of the cross are reared in very different environments, and each parent possesses some quality deficient in the other.

In former times the question of wool was of great importance, and on this count Border Leicester parentage, for example, was regarded very favourably.   At the present time the Cheviot Border Leicester half bred gives the famous " north wool " for the Bradford market. To-day the main value of the cross relates to meat.   As a rule the lowland sheep has the larger frame, age for age, than the upland, whereas the latter possesses the better quality meat.   Hence it is a common practice to put ewes drafted from the hill breeding flocks to lowland rams.   The result is a lamb both larger and of earlier maturity than the purely hill breeds, and having a meat flavour greatly surpassing that of the purely lowland lamb.   The draft ewe, after the birth of one or two lambs, is usually fattened to give excellent mutton, but hill breeds kept permanently on the lowlands, even though breeding true for successive generations, would lose the good meat flavour, whereas " lowland sheep " do badly on " upland " fare.

The desire to utilize poor pastures situated amid better ones has led to definite invasions of suitable breeds from distant sources.   For example, the Yorkshire moors will not support large-bodied sheep, and Scotch Blackfaces have been established upon them.   The largish Wensleydale sheep occupy the high dales intersecting these moors.   A cross of Blackface ewe and Wensleydale ram, when fattened, gives good lamb or mutton, and the hardy rams at coupling time follow the ewes over the roughest places of the moors, so that the ewes need not be drafted from the flock and sent below.   This sheep husbandry has been established since about 1877, and is found also in Cumberland and Westmorland, whither the Wensleydales have extended their range.   The half breds are the Mashams.[1]   The Cumberland Mashams come from their hills in tens of thousands, and when fed in the local lowlands or those of the eastern counties on turnips and grass, they are ready for the butcher from nine to eighteen months.   Many of them graze in the London Parks.

The popularity of the Border Leicester cross is due to its early maturity, its economical fattening and its power of handing on these qualities to its offspring.   It is said to pay more rents in the arable parts of Scotland and Northumberland than any other variety of sheep in Britain.   Its half bred lambs [2] (sometimes known as Barmshires and sometimes as " grey-faces ") are ready for the winter fattening.   The draft Blackface ewes required for this latter cross are sold in tens of thousands at the autumn auction sale in Penrith.   The Border Leicester Herdwick cross is very suitable for high tillage farms.

The Cheviot Lincoln cross is very popular on the Northumberland lowlands, good quality lamb and

---

[1] The Cheviot Wensleydale cross is also a Masham.
[2] This cross is known as a cross bred rather than " half bred ", because, unlike most half breds, it will breed true to type.

mutton resulting from it.  The half bred ewes of this and the Cheviot Border Leicester cross are sometimes mated with the Border Leicester or half bred rams.  The Cheviot is also used for crossing with the Suffolk and Shropshire.

The desire for half breds may be due directly to the need for a more arable sheep in regions where native arable sheep are lacking.  This is the case in the counties of Buckingham, Bedford, Northampton and Cambridge. The four-course system of rotation requires an arable sheep not necessarily for permanent keep as breeding stock, but for quick fattening.  The type has no time to alter and no breeding is done.  Oxford Down and Hampshire crosses are here employed, the somewhat wet lair being of no disadvantage to a cross with Cotswold blood. Sometimes it is a grazing sheep that is needed, especially at the present, when arable farming is on the decline. The establishment of crosses between the native sheep and the Cheviot, Scotch Blackface and Exmoors on our South Downs is a case in point.

The Cotswold ram-Hampshire ewe cross gives a lamb that can be fattened early on grass ; the Lincoln and Leicester cross gives Wold sheep, wintering out of doors in a cold climate because of the Leicester element with its endowment of fat, whereby protection is afforded during cold and wet close folding.  The large lambs, or hoggs, indeed, have rather too much fat for present tastes.  A Romney Marsh and Southdown or Hampshire cross gives a sheep of early maturity and folding value —the mutton is good and in demand for the seaside resorts of Kent and Sussex.

The first cross between particular parents are always of a recognized type, but when half breds are paired, some of the offspring may resemble the granddam and some the grandsire, and not the intermediate parents, and it by no means follows that the second generation will retain the qualities for which the original mating was projected. Thus a race of mongrels of indefinite type is produced as the interbreeding continues down the generations, and in general the original half breds are not allowed to mate. Some exceptions are the Cheviot or Blackface cross with the Border Leicester, bred on the high arable farms of the Border counties, half bred ewes and rams bred on identical lines, or the half bred ewes are crossed with Border Leicester, Suffolk, or Oxford Down rams. The offspring of this second generation give solid, lean mutton. What has just been said in no way invalidates what was said earlier upon the improvement of native strains, and the making of true cross breds. For these latter were the outcome of slow and often costly experiment until the right amount of influence of the contributing breeds had been properly adjusted. The primary object was to create good breeding flocks, whereas many of the new experiments are concerned only with producing lamb.

In this chapter we have considered how the ancient breeds, uniquely capable of occupying their traditional environments, have acquired new vigour by the infusion of a little alien blood or become more adaptable to the native environment, itself undergoing progressive changes. We have seen how new types better fitted to modern requirements, and showing some improvement in wool or meat or both, have been developed, including sheep needed to eat up good or poor pastures. We have come finally to the half breds, destined for special purposes—wool in former times, lamb or mutton to-day. In this last case we should particularly notice the juxtaposition of complementary geographical environments, the mountain or hill country—the realm of the ewes—for the breeding stock and, but much less than formerly, wethers for hill mutton of various ages, and the lowlands where forage crops or good grass is to be eaten by sheep of larger body but less well-flavoured meat. Hither come the oldest ewes, drafted from the hill flocks, and, mating with lowland rams, produce lambs that have a propensity derived from their sires to fatten easily on the plentiful food provided, and from their dams, to give meat, lamb or mutton, of " sweet " hill flavour.

M

CHAPTER XV

IMPROVED BREEDS OF CATTLE

AS in the case of sheep, some cattle thrive better in wet than in dry places, some flourish upon the heavy and cold soils which are anathema to others. Some need a rich food, others make the utmost use of poor and scant fare. Such factors as these must be taken into account when breeds are selected for particular districts. In autumn young Sussex cattle will graze and improve upon the poor and cold Weald pasture, where shorthorns would quickly lose flesh, though the latter, fed on rich pastures and a plentiful winter food, will do so well that the heavy expense of this rearing is justified. The wilder breeds, Welsh, Shetland, Kerry, Dexter, and Highland cattle, will grow when kept in yards on a diet mainly of straw browse and roots.

In the case of cattle, the making of new breeds or the improvement of old ones does not necessitate such a complete adaptation to environment as in the case of sheep, for in general cattle live under a more domestic régime than the less tamed sheep, and where an " improvement " has resulted in some weakening of constitution, this weakening is much discounted by the food and shelter supplied by man.

The peculiar advantages of the true cross breds in the sheep world are obtained amongst cattle more generally by improvement within the breed.

Cattle have been distinguished as long horned, middle horned, and short horned, polled or hornless, but except

164

that long horns are out of place in yard or stall where beasts may be crowded together such a classification has no geographical significance.  On the other hand the purpose for which cattle are kept introduces the question of feeding grounds, whether grass or arable, a matter of real geographical import.  The dairyman rears primarily for milk, the breeder for stores, the grazier for grass fattening, the feeder for fattening largely under cover.  The small farmer, on his part, usually engages in two or more of these activities.

Cattle may be classified into milk, meat, and dual purpose breeds.  In the latter case the beef is of good quality and the cows good milkers.

The Ayrshire and Lincoln Reds are good examples of the purely milk breeds.  The Ayrshires have already been considered.  The breed is too small for the best English grasslands, which to be " eaten over " properly would require a large number of Ayrshires involving much more attention than the smaller number of dairy cattle of English breeds.  The Ayrshire is in demand, however, as a dairy cow in districts round London and elsewhere.

The Lincoln Reds are shorthorns, and shorthorn blood may have been introduced into the county during the early stages of the improvement of the great Teeswater breed, for Culley noted an improvement between two visits paid to Lincolnshire at the end of the eighteenth century.  Three bulls of the Collings herd were also taken thither in 1810, to help in the improvement of the breed.  The Lincoln Red is the cow of the small farmer growing beans, wheat, and turnips.  The cattle are wintered on roots and cake in the farmyard, but are placed upon marshes and grasslands in spring.  Life under conditions including much exposure to easterly winds has evolved a hardy race of stock, quick to fatten and good " at the pail ".

Among the beef breeds may be mentioned the Aberdeen-Angus, the Highland and Galloway cattle, all of Scotland. The Aberdeen-Angus has already been considered in detail. The famous West Highland cattle, the original breed of West and much of Northern Scotland, where the climate and herbage are more suited to it than to any other breed of cattle, is perhaps the oldest and purest of the bovine races in the United Kingdom. At the beginning of the nineteenth century Glen Lyon and the Trossachs country became famous for Highland cattle. They were bred here by the Stewart family and taken to Lewis in 1802, and a few years later to Harris, where crossing of best Perthshire bulls with the best Island cows gave a herd of great excellence. The alternative name of Kyloes signifies " aboriginal ", and as shaggy, hardy, comparatively small " runts " they are to be found pure in Skye and other islands of the Hebrides, and also in the Highlands of Inverness, Perth, and Dumbarton. The hair and horns of the Island cattle owe their peculiar development to the wet climate, mild winter, and quality of the pasturage. The better favoured pastures of Perth, Ross, Argyll, Dumbarton, Nairn and Inverness carry a larger breed. Their spread to those countries from their original Highland home dates from about 1883. On the succulent yellow turnips of Aberdeen and the rich pastures of the other counties just mentioned, they develop into the great beasts which rank with the best. As a mountain breed they mature late, and good as is the meat, this delayed maturity also delays the interest on the capital outlay, hence West Highlanders are less favourable to the lowland farmer buying them for finishing at about two years old with heavy expenses in feeding stuffs than to the highland, who raises them cheaply as stores on the rough natural hill pastures in the summer, and on meadow hay or straw in the winter, in addition to what they can pick up for themselves.

Management of these cattle varies considerably with the district and size of the herd. When kept in large numbers they can remain all the year in the open with the exception of the breeding cows, which are supplied with pens and sheds at calving time (January to March or April), after which the calves run with their mothers till weaned about the beginning of October. Where there is mixed farming, as in Inverness, the breeding cows are housed and milked, and the calves reared by hand on arable. The milk, though small in quantity, is rich.

The Galloways are extensively reared both sides of the Solway. They appear to be descended from the same stock as the shaggier Kyloes, for in remote times the breed extended over Ayrshire and to the Caledonian Canal rift. The modern Galloway is probably derived from a fusion of old breeds in ancient Galloway (Kirkcudbright and Wigtownshire) and Cumberland consequent on the feuds of the Scotch and English Border landowners. Well known as early as the beginning of the sixteenth century, the Galloways remained small in number through much of the eighteenth century, as sheep for wool was a staple of the region. After the union of England and Scotland the demand in the English Eastern Counties for store cattle for fattening encouraged the herding of Galloways, and down to about 1810, they held the field in the Scottish Border territory. Towards the end of the eighteenth century southern drovers were collecting them from the neighbourhood of Dumfries, and taking 25,000 to 35,000 four-year-olds to the rich pastures of Lincoln and Northampton or the salt marshes of Norfolk and Suffolk to be " finished off " for the Smithfield market in London. The rich fattening pastures of Wigtown and Dumfries also obtained their quota.

The profits derived by sale of their stores encouraged the breeders of Galloways to attempt some improvement, which was finally brought about (1825–50) not by crossing, but by selection of good stock, good feeding, and good management, wealthy landlords persuading and assisting their tenants to this end. Further betterment during the next half-century was a result of the incentive given by the annual show and sale of young bulls instituted at Lockerbie in 1851 and at Castle Douglas in 1855. A herd book was also established, and drew attention to the merits of the Galloway. The earlier dun and brindled colouring has disappeared, but except for its present black colour the type has not greatly changed.

The Galloway is generally classed with the mountain breeds. It is hornless, and when well bred has two coats, of which the outer is of wavy but not curly hair, while the under coat is short and thick, and soft as silk. This covering keeps out cold but keeps in heat, and so almost all young Galloways, including heifers till they drop their first calf, can be kept in open fields, and without shelter, both summer and winter.

Since 1857 the Galloway has been ousted to some extent from its home quarters in favour of dairy Ayrshire cows and the feeding of cross bred sheep. The improvement and reclamation of waste lands and the extended growth of forage crops is increasing the cultivated area. This is especially so in the Stuartry, where there is much arable for fattening of cross breds, whereas store cattle cannot be hurried up. Moreover, the Norfolk feeder nowadays asks almost entirely for Irish beasts. The Galloway is now kept upon many Ayrshire farms, receiving a winter fattening, but here its dung is as important as its beef. In the Smithfield market the Galloway beef is styled " prime Scots ". It is tender, and the fat and lean well mixed, all popular qualities. The cow gives a fair quantity of milk when carefully managed, but is not a dairy cow.

The Scotch shorthorn, our fourth example of the Scotch great beef breeds, has a somewhat unique history. The development of the English Dairy shorthorn has already been considered. After 1860 two types of shorthorns were widely recognized.

About 1840 a herd was founded by Cruickshank of Sittyton, Aberdeen, for which the best bulls of a certain kind had been purchased from England, but it was not until the birth of the bull " Champion of England ", in 1860, that success was really attained. The breeding resulted in an animal almost perfect as a meat producer, but with milking capacity largely lost. The herd was sold in 1890, by which time this Scotch shorthorn had become quite fashionable in England.

One of our earliest known English beef breeds is the Sussex, first mentioned in records about the time of the Norman Conquest, and then, as now, more or less limited to Pevensey and the surrounding districts. The Sussex cattle were originally bred for draught oxen and became " meat " only when their heavy field labour on the Weald was over. Even when the use of oxen for field work had been replaced by horses, the Sussex ox was used to pull vehicles bound for London over the heavy Wealden clay, and they were still used for draught as late as 1890. However, its flesh was early recognized to be of fine quality, and when no longer needed for the plough, the draft oxen of East Sussex and West Kent were sold at the fairs of Battle, Lewes, etc., and bought by the West Sussex farmer for a year's grazing before slaughter.

The original Sussex cattle was long legged, strong boned, and specially fitted for burden. Since about 1886 breeding from the smaller boned animals with the greatest amount of flesh has effected improvements in the beef and general appearance, and to-day the rearing is only for the beef. The cattle cross with any breed, red being the usual colour of the offspring. The animals are hardy, thriving on the poorest pastures of their native county. When fattened they lay on flesh rapidly. In the days of the great joint the fat bullocks of this herd, like those of the West Highland cattle formerly, were greatly in demand at Christmas.

Another English beef breed is the Hereford, a middle horn, and indigenous to its county of name. This breed has existed in a state of purity perhaps longer than any other of the so-called pure breeds now in existence. The records of King John's reign refer to it in a eulogistic manner (Holinshed). On the other hand, Benjamin Tompkins (1745–1815) is sometimes regarded as the founder of the breed as we know it, but he may have been only a prominent breeder imposing some particular strain.

The original home of the Hereford was the plain of Hereford, low lying and generally fertile, with a soil of the old Red Sandstone series consisting of clay, marl, and some other calcareous material. There is much permanent pasture. The rearing of Herefords was principally in the hands of tenant farmers, who have handed down their farm stock, in all its purity, from father to son through many generations, thus perpetuating the good meat qualities—taste, rapid fattening, and good proportion of lean and fat. The steers have long been in demand by graziers of the midland and eastern counties, and this sale provides the main return of the farming. The Hereford also gives a hardy cross with the little black Welsh cows, and this cross can be fed up to give a good weight of good meat.

The Hereford has a red body and a white mottled face ; it matures early, giving a great weight of beef which some regard as slightly superior to shorthorn beef. It is an excellent grazing breed, fattening to perfection on grass, the best beef going to London. It can do well on other diets, however, and so has extended its range to Shropshire, Warwickshire, Staffordshire, Dorset, and Cornwall. Herefords have also supplanted the native cattle of Glamorgan, Brecknock, Radnor, and Montgomery, and are to be found in other parts of Wales. The cows live on the pastures for the greater part of the year, and when taken to the farm in winter get turnips, straw, or hay. Young stock not intended for shows generally spend all the year on the pasture.

We have now to consider the dual purpose cattle of Britain : all the cattle, male and female, give good meat, and the cows give " good " milk.

While the making of the Scotch shorthorn was in progress English farmers, working upon old lines, succeeded in evolving the dual purpose or dairy shorthorn. The original material was the unimproved shorthorn that went on foot in great droves from the north to the south of England, giving opportunities for the farmers en route to buy the best animals for their home stock.

The shorthorn is a big-framed, gentle beast, in colour red, white, red and white, roan or roan and white ; it produces more milk from the same quantity of food than any other breed, which, though not of really best quality, passes the standard of the milk trade. Some consider the beef a little inferior, but with equal advantage the shorthorn makes more and earlier beef than any other breed. No animal responds more to good feeding, and the steers, like the discarded dairy cows, can usually be fed for profitable beef production.

The great merit of the shorthorn is its power of crossing with and improving other breeds. The cattle of Ireland (once noted for its mongrel stock) have been immeasurably improved by the shorthorn, while in Scotland the crossing of shorthorns and native cattle produces magnificent half breeds. The excellent milking properties of the dairy shorthorn have made the breed profitable to dairymen and graziers alike. It flourishes upon a variety of different soils, such as those of the Holderness district of Yorkshire, the heavy soils of the Fylde of Lancashire, the Derbyshire limestone, and the keuper marl of Cheshire. Its adaptability to different climates and soils, its faculty of simultaneous fattening and growth, its very early maturity, its ability to give its calves abundant milk, are qualities for which the shorthorn was praised in 1875,[1] and which it still possesses. Little more than 150 years ago the breed was local; now it is world-wide. It has displaced other breeds in part or in whole over large areas. The midland longhorn has been utterly displaced, lingering only in gentlemen's parks; in Wales this shorthorn now outnumbers the Castle Martin cattle and Welsh runts in their own home, and pure bred shorthorns are found in North and South Wales, and the Islands of Man, Orkneys, and Shetlands.

On account of their dual purpose properties the City and suburban dairyman buys young shorthorn cows after the first calving and keeps them on forcing food for ten to twelve months. By this time the milk has dropped to about a gallon a day, and the cow is fat and ready for the butcher.

[1] *The Cattle, Sheep, and Pigs of Great Britain.* Edited by Colman, 1887, 1st edition, pp. 110–41.

The English longhorn is another, but more ancient dual purpose breed. About one hundred and fifty years ago this breed was the most valuable one in South Britain, and from its original home in the Craven district of Yorkshire it had spread to the neighbouring midlands, Lancashire, and to south-eastern Westmorland. The earliest important experiments in improving cattle were based on the longhorn, whose *long horn*, however, was a disqualification, and the breed passed out of favour. To its picturesque aspect it owes its continued existence in gentlemen's parks, and it has even been " improved " of late years. It matures late, gives milk richer in quality but less in quantity than do the polled cows, and is so hardy that only cows in milk and very young calves require special housing.

The Norfolk and Suffolk Red Polled cattle have a complex origin. The cattle of north Norfolk were described by Marshall [1] as having flesh of superior quality and as " a small, hardy, thriving race, clean, middle, but curving, horns, favourite colour blood red and white, or mottled face ". The original breed may have been introduced by Danes of the eleventh century. Records exist of a polled breed upon the Norfolk–Suffolk border and farther south : originally dun and later red, red and white or brindled, the cows gave milk at that time (*c.* 1735) regarded as the best among English cows. This Suffolk breed probably owes its introduction to the Angle-folk, who kept a hornless breed of cattle.

During " droving days " this original stock was crossed with polled Galloway bulls, calling into existence the polled breed of Norfolk as well as Suffolk. Later John Reeve Wighton, a tenant of Coke of Holkham, and Richard England of Binham, endeavoured to evolve a dual purpose cow. Selecting prime red Norfolk and

[1] *Rural Economy of Norfolk* (1780–2).

Suffolk polled milkers, they mated them with a certain Norfolk blood-red bull. Mr. Reeve showed the new stock at the Holkham sheep shearing of 1810, and its good qualities recommended it to the great local cattle breeders, who, working on this new " blood-red " stock, co-operated in fixing the type. Subsequently the prizes offered by the National Agricultural Society and the cups and gifts of private donors stimulated breeders to make further improvements. The Suffolk breed is the better milker, whereas the Norfolk gives the better beef ; the quality of the meat, however, though good, is distinctly inferior to that of the special beef breeds or the dual purpose shorthorn, but there is a market for small superior joints.

The breed is a hardy one, thriving on the scanty herbage, severe winters, and peculiarly cold springs of East Anglia ; it is a good milking breed, with the rather unusual faculty of carrying on the milk supply from one calving to another. The Suffolk ranks high among the polled breeds for dairy purposes when the pastures are mediocre, being more suitable for upland fields, but this cow is rarely met with outside its home counties.

The Devon dual purpose cattle have also a slight bias as " beef producing Devons " and " dairy Devons ".

The North Devons are a middle horned breed of remote ancestry, probably akin to the native Hereford, Sussex, Welsh, and Scotch breeds, but differentiated by soil, climate, time, and human management. Improvement has gradually been effected by selection. The cattle are admirably adapted by their habits and hardiness to feed on the moors. The rich quality of their milk produces good butter and the well-known Devonshire cream. In colour the cattle vary from a dark red to a light red and chestnut ; they are lean, active, small. The ox was used for draught up to 1911, and after five or six years' labour in the field was fattened for beef. The breed feeds economically, fattening quickly under suitable diet, and giving much meat in proportion to the food consumed. North Devon cattle are kept extensively in the great cheese districts of Somerset and Dorset, and are also found in Cornwall.

The South Devon cattle are similar but inferior. They fatten rapidly in stall or on pasture, and may be found on Dartmoor. A third variety, known as the Somerset Devon, is perhaps merely a matter of locality, but all three branches of the Devon cattle are much alike.

From time immemorial the mountains and valleys of Wales have been noted for their fine herds of grazing cattle, and ever since the earliest droving days were annually sold in their thousands at the local cattle fairs and taken for rapid fattening to the grazing districts of the English Midlands and the marshes of the south-east.

In the earlier years of the nineteenth century Wales could boast of several breeds generally designated " black cattle " or " runts "—in the south were the red, smoky-faced " Montgomeries " (now practically extinct owing to displacement by the shorthorn), " Glamorgans " and the " Castle Martins " or Pembrokeshire breed ; in the north were the " Angleseys ", famous then as now. Crossing has been attempted between the Welsh and some British breeds, but without much success. Improvements have resulted by attention to desired qualities. Actually at the end of the nineteenth century the difference in these north and south breeds, due to difference in management and some crossing, was very slight, and in 1904 their herd books were combined. This amalgamation into one great family of Welsh black cattle and the institution of Welsh national shows have been of very great help in their progress.

The Welsh cattle mature early and its good quality makes their meat popular.

The runt is merely the native cattle badly managed as the cottager's cow, but when grazed on the good pastures of the Severn Valley and the Midlands, it thrives gloriously and takes an honoured place at the Christmas Fat Stock Shows for the London market.

The Angleseys occupy that island and much of North Wales; climate and soil conspire to produce a hardy breed which is slightly lighter in colour than the Pembrokes. Anglesey has always been the home of herds of prolific cows whose progeny went in great numbers to the mainland, originally as food for North Wales, and later for pasturing in the English counties. In 1649 Anglesey exported annually 3,000 cattle, which swam the Menai Straits, few being drowned. After the construction of the Menai Bridge this export increased to 10,000. The young stock are of a high class and respond to feeding on swedes, turnips, etc., and are often fed in the open yard, where, on oats and straw, they become steers of great size. They give good beef; the cows could be good milkers and are easily fattened for meat after service, but their milking qualities are much neglected.

It may be recalled that part of Pembroke early came under English domination, but high farming on the English plan was not possible. The great humidity is very favourable to grass, with oats as staple cereal rather than wheat. The hill country of Pembroke contains some of the best pastures, but they are exposed to storms of wind and rain in autumn and winter. Farmyards with sufficient accommodation for feeding and breeding are not frequent and the general conditions, which include winter in the open and night housing

in exceptionally severe weather only, are more suited
for the native breed.

The native Castle Martin breed is hardy, slow in
maturing, and over large areas has been displaced by
more rapidly maturing shorthorns, Herefords, and their
crosses, and out-numbered in others.   The milk and its
products have a market in South Wales.

It is related of the Glamorgans, that in the twelfth
century, one Sir Robert Fitzhammond, a Norman knight,
introduced some Normandy cattle, whose crossing with
the native cattle produced the Glamorgan breed.   There
also appears to have been a later infusion of Devon
blood acquired during the latter part of the eighteenth
century, by a local magnate called Sir Richard de
Grenvaille.   Neither of these alien strains has greatly
influenced the stock.   Onwards from the eighteenth
century Glamorgan farmers took great pride in the breed
and endeavoured to keep it pure.   At that time grazing
cattle were in high demand, there being no stall feeding
and no improved shorthorn.   The females were hardy
and profitable milkers, the males active, docile, excellent
for plough and cart, and capable of being fattened after
six to seven years' service into a good and profitable
beef, which was done on the rich English pastures as
the cattle made their way to London.

George III stocked his farm at Windsor with Glamorgans, with periodic recruitments of fresh blood from
the Welsh fairs.   To-day Glamorgans have fallen from
favour, and even in their home counties of Glamorgan,
Monmouth, and Gloucester, they have declined in character and numbers, and are no longer bred pure.

The native cattle of the Shetland Islands are small
but robust.   They were early cut off from admixture
with the mainland breeds, and the type has developed
under conditions of inferior feeding grounds and a severe

climate.  They are bred by the cottars and small holders
and until 2 or 3 years old run at large on the scathold
all the year round, though they are stalled at night
in winter and given a handful of straw.  At the time
of the May sales they are thin and emaciated, but the
graziers who buy them put them on good grass, often
on one of the islets.  They soon put on flesh, and by
October or November are ready for sale as " fat " cattle.
The cows produce abundant milk in proportion to their
size.  Discarded cows are also sold off in May for good
summer grazing.  They are killed in autumn for home
needs, or exported to Aberdeen or Edinburgh as *marts*.

During the 'sixties some attempt was made to improve
the native cattle of the Shetlands ;  the first cattle
show was held at Lerwick in 1864, and the Highland
Society began to give prizes for other pure breeds beside
the native cattle.  This was to encourage the keeping
of good stock for crossing or improving, and to-day good
pedigreed shorthorns and polled Angus bulls are to be
found here and in the Orkneys, whereby some increase
of size has been produced.

We have now to consider the cross breds which, with
cattle, take the place of the half breds considered in
the previous chapter.  Here, too, and for similar reasons
as in the case of sheep, it is not usual to breed beyond
the first generation.

The cross with the Aberdeen-Angus is mainly to
enhance the beef qualities of the other partner.  Its
first crossing with the white shorthorn cow produces a
grey or black half bred (blue-greys) of great feeding
capacity.  The cross, marketed in large numbers in
the north of Scotland centres, is bought extensively for
the midland and southern counties of England, where it
has largely replaced the West Highland steers especially
since the 1880–90 decline in the numbers reared of

the latter. The Aberdeen-Angus bulls have an extensive sale, many going to pure bred herds. Cross bred Aberdeen-Angus beef is even produced in the arable districts of the Cotswolds. In recent years Irish-bred shorthorn heifers of good type have been crossed with the polled Angus bull. This bull is also mated with the Ayrshire cow, the calves of the cross being sold to feeders at 2–3 weeks old. The cross here and of the shorthorn bull and Ayrshire cow realizes better prices than the pure bred Ayrshire calf.

The crosses with the shorthorn are also numerous. Besides those mentioned above there is that of the white shorthorn bull and the Galloway cow, also a " blue-grey ", famous throughout the Border. The calves of this cross are of all colours ; the mature animals are great feeders and give superior beef. They are mostly reared in Galloway or about the Border, and sold in the Carlisle market. A similar cross of the shorthorn cow and Galloway bull is also reared in the north of England. This " blue-grey " cross is of earlier maturity, and gives beautifully " mixed " flesh. Other shorthorn crosses are with the West Highlanders, Shetlanders, and Channel Islands' breeds, these last giving good meat and high quality milk.

The Ayrshire cow and Galloway bull give a hardy cross, black in colour, of early maturity, and good beef. This cross is bred largely on Galloway farms where dairying (with Ayrshire cows) is carried on as well as some feeding and rearing of cattle.

Some breeds of foreign origin have been kept for so long in Britain, that they should be mentioned. The Dutch Frisian is very popular in East Anglia, where dairying is spreading. In the Jerseys and Guernseys the Channel Islands have provided some noted milk breeds. The clotted cream of the smaller farms of

N

Cornwall is often made from the milk of Guernseys, albeit not always pure bred.   The Jerseys are the richest milkers and are the best butter producers in the world, if quality, quantity, and colour be all taken into account. Not being a beef breed, the male calves are killed young for producing excellent veal.

Not very long ago, much of the cattle grazed in Northumberland was Irish, and of Irish shorthorn pattern.   The introduction of Irish cattle into Scotland has some interesting features.   Fifty years ago the grass-fed Irish two year olds, or stirks, were coming over to the Falkirk Tryst in spring, and after sale, fed upon turnips in Fife and East Lothian, finding their way by degrees to the arable farms of the Moray Firth lowlands.   The importation of Irish cattle for fattening and slaughter went on steadily.   In 1933 store cattle embarked at Dublin were landed at Liverpool, Birkenhead, Heysham, etc., and taken inland for distribution to the Midlands, East Anglia, and Wales.   Fat cattle, embarking also at Dublin, are slaughtered on reaching Liverpool.

The Kerry cattle originated in the Irish county of that name, and they belong to the curved, or middle horn class.   Kerry cattle reared in England are discriminated as the Dexter Kerries.   The Kerries are usually black, but may be red ; small on their home mountains, they improve in size, form and condition on English pastures.   The improved Kerry is the breed kept in Britain, an excellent milk breed, which the Kerry " Kerries " are not.

The Dexter breed is an off-shoot of the native Irish Kerries formed by a Mr. Dexter by selection of the best mountain cattle of the district.   It combines the feeding and milking properties suitable for villa residents, and fattens rapidly when permitted on moderate pasture, giving fine and well-flavoured beef. It is said that this docile, easily kept cow of the poor man was introduced into England by Sir Robert Peel and others about the middle of the nineteenth century.

This chapter has been concerned with the pure breds and their crosses, but it must be recognized that animals *outside* the pure bred herds form the general farm stock of the country, especially of the small holder. As regards special localities devoted to milk, meat, stores, it may be stated broadly that where the soil is fertile and the rain not too excessive, so that good arable crops can be raised, we may expect to find the domain of the *beef* cattle. Beef cattle are also a feature of the richer grasslands, while stores feed sufficiently on the poorer. The needs of man for milk and milk products, however, may upset these simple distributions, especially where road and rail facilities for long distances and quick horse or motor transport for local collection may make milk production more profitable. Combined grass and stall-feeding may give some milk supply for the great towns, but these latter are now so much nearer the great grazing districts through the new means of swift transport, that even in store and fattening districts there is often very profitable rearing for milk, a commodity that gives quick returns on capital outlay. The accompanying diagram, giving store and fattening cattle districts of England and Wales, together with the special dairy regions feeding London, will tell its own story.

# PART III
# THE LEGACY

## CHAPTER XVI

## THE PRODUCTS OF THE INDUSTRY

IN the previous chapters we have traced the Pastoral Industry of Britain from its obscure beginnings, through the marvellous progress in foods and breeds of the eighteenth and following centuries, to the sheep and cattle of Britain as we know them to-day.

We have seen how, in former times, cattle were raised for labour or milk, sheep for their wool, and only killed for their meat when their period of service was over, or if annual birth were in excess of these requirements, an autumn slaughter was necessitated by the poverty of the winter food supplies. We have seen how a great meat trade rose on the ashes of the trade in wool, the early enthusiasm leading to the rearing of larger animals with some improvement in quality of meat, though large fat joints and aged mutton were ideal meats barely fifty years ago. Since that time the meat industry has changed considerably, the smaller families of to-day requiring small, tender joints, emanating from small young animals, though for special occasions and in large restaurants and hotels some " mighty beef " still appears upon the table. The new taste meets the farmer's approval, for the price of English meat has been lowered by foreign competition, and the cost of production is also reduced when the stock matures quickly and is killed off young. Nowadays all cattle, except the dairy stock and necessary bulls, all sheep except breeding ewes and rams, and the cattle or sheep required for export, are killed young. Old beef and mutton are derived from discarded dairy cows and draft ewes; the life of a dairy cow is about 4½ years..

The cattle of the British Isles are reared for beef and the dairy in about equal proportions, Scotland supplying about a third of the beef of Great Britain; Irish stores fattened in Britain are included in this figure.

During the last few years, much of our beef produced by yard feeding in autumn is being replaced by grass fattening in summer. In Norfolk and Suffolk the dehorned short-horned bullock is being kept on arable but in store condition throughout the winter, as a preliminary to the summer grass fattening.

The vigorous industry connected with the raising of good flavoured, early maturing half bred lambs has already been noted. Lambs make up about 90 per cent of the sheep sold for slaughter in Britain, for their meat is tender and their joints small. Spring lambs are young lambs dropped during the winter and sold at three to five months. Wethers are killed young; yearling wethers are used as a substitute for lamb meat, but yearling ewes, maturing earlier, are not so good for this purpose.

One quarter of the sheep meat of Great Britain comes from Scotland, apart from the large numbers of store sheep and draft breeding ewes sold annually from Scotland for fattening on English farms. The production of fat lamb has made great strides since the beginning of the century. The annual production of mutton and lamb meat is about 3½ million cwt. Mutton sheep are most numerous in the hill districts of the north and west, where there is much rough grazing, and where this kind of pastoral farming has been definitely on the increase during the last fifty years.

Lowland farmers often possess land unsuitable for a permanent flock, and since the War there has been a great increase in the keeping of flying flocks of lambs and draft ewes which may feed on temporary leys.   The lowland areas of Wales and the eastern counties of Scotland feed vast numbers of these half bred lambs for sale in summer and autumn.   Grass fattening in summer is also practised in the South Down region ;  Dorset, Gloucester, Somerset, all breed to produce early lambs for Easter sale, when prices are high.   In the English Midlands a cross with Shropshire rams and white-faced ewes also provide early and rapidly maturing lambs.

Upon the shoulders of our sheep has risen a British Industry anciently of supreme importance.   It was based upon the large number of British breeds made possible by the differences in the soil and climate of their habitats, differences which provide a geographical basis for the special characteristics of the wool with regard to staple, texture, lustre, felting properties, etc. These diverse qualities made our wool particularly marketable.

There is nothing to prove that sheep were not kept in Britain in very remote times.   Bones resembling sheep bones have been found in the débris of the Somerset Lake villages.   Caesar makes no mention of sheep in Britain, but his personal knowledge of our country was limited to a very small corner of it.   Early in the Roman occupation there was an important manufacture of fine woollen cloth at Winchester, and Roman writers eulogized British wool as comparable to a spider's thread for purity and fineness.   Spinning and weaving are referred to in Anglo-Saxon literature, the fleeces being spun from the distaff by the females of the household, no matter what their rank.   At first individual families kept but a few sheep, using all the wool for the domestic needs ;   later there was an export of woollen cloth (eighth century).  After the Norman Conquest the wool industry became very flourishing ;  the Cotswolds, for example, were converted into vast sheep walks, and much wool was produced for sale at home and abroad. During and onwards from the twelfth century, the duty on exported wool brought great wealth to the English crown.  The ransom of Richard I was paid largely out of the wool tax.  The wool trade reached its first high water mark in the thirteenth century, the succeeding decline being due to political troubles that adversely affected the cloth-making centres.  The Black Death of the fourteenth century gave another impetus to the wool production, again bringing much foreign money into the country.  The English kings of this period encouraged the making of a saleable cloth for export, which would also provide good cloth for home use and so reduce the import.  For example, Edward III (1327–77) granted special protection to weavers, dyers and fullers from Flanders to settle in England, make up English wool, and teach their trade.  The export trade in wool also recovered.  It was largely seasonal, the shorn wool being sent across the Channel in summer and the fells (skins with adhesive wool) in autumn and winter.  To collect the export duty on wool more easily and to give more opportunity for such government inspection as might prevent fraudulent packing of the wool sacks likely to discredit English wool abroad, Acts of Parliament were passed (c. 1353) enforcing the shipment of pastoral (and other) products from a few specified ports—the staple ports—but this legislation soon fell into abeyance owing to the preference of the merchants and their foreign buyers for personal meetings. During the Middle Ages the three areas of textile manufacture were the West Country (Gloucester, Wiltshire, Somerset), East Anglia (particularly Suffolk and Essex), and Yorkshire, at that time third in both quality and quantity. By the middle of the fifteenth century, Flanders, Italy and even more remote countries were receiving our wool. By the end of that century England had become largely a nation of sheep farmers and cloth makers.

During the sixteenth, seventeenth and eighteenth centuries, there was a great expansion of the woollen and worsted industries, the different districts with their different quality wool producing different classes of goods. These were the centuries of the great mercantile companies of Clothiers and Drapers, buying the wool from the farmers and distributing it for spinning and weaving, the cloth being sold locally in specially built markets—the Cloth Halls—or at the London Cloth Fair.

The Companies used their surplus wealth for the expansion of industry and trade, and refugee foreign workmen lent their knowledge and skill. Further, foreign manufactures suffered during these centuries of Continental turmoil, so that England captured much of the foreign market hitherto closed to it. By the end of the seventeenth century, woollen goods made up two-thirds of the value of the English export trade. Scotland too had its export trade, which (sixteenth century) was mainly in wool for Flanders and the Netherlands, but was also in exporting coarse woollen cloth to France, and wool, skins, and yarn to England. Almost all the wool exported was the longwool, Cotswold being most in demand, though Lincoln lustre was also in favour. The short wool was used at home, since it could not compete with the merino. However, the broadcloth made from the short wool found a good market on the Continent.

Towards the end of this period England became

involved in the movement known as the Industrial Revolution (*c.* 1750–1850) whereby new inventions speeded up processes of spinning and weaving and the manufacture of cloth as a domestic industry gave way to the immensely larger quantities manufactured under the factory system. This necessitated greatly increased supplies of raw material, and 1850 marks the beginning of the era of our huge import of foreign wool. As the sheep of Britain are now reared for meat, our wool is less fine than foreign wool, where breeding for quality of wool is still much practised.

It is now an opportune moment to recall what has been said upon the more purely geographical side of the subject. The best wool in Britain comes from sheep fed on open downs or drained marshes, regions colder than the Midland lowlands, where the wool is not of as much value. The mineral matter passing from the soil into the herbage influences the character of the wool of the sheep fed upon that herbage. The softest woolled sheep feed on pastures derived from clayey and sandy soils (neutral and acid mineral soils), while the " calcareous " wools of sheep pasturing upon the grass of a limestone or chalky soil are harsh, dry and do not felt well. The heavy lands seem more suited to the sheep of the long, lustrous wool, and the lighter and more chalky lands to the short-woolled Down breeds. Apart from the staple, wools differ from each other in fineness and in other ways ; hence their suitability for a variety of fabrics which are classified on broad lines as woollens and worsteds. The long lustre wools of England are probably inferior to none for such wool. These wools are combed and spun by the worsted process ; about 90 per cent of British fleeces are from long-woolled sheep. The medium wools are employed for imitation serges, tweeds, etc. The short fine wools of the Southdowns are worked up for the true woollens—knitting yarn, hosiery, flannels, for which their crimpiness is an asset.

Some of the mountain breeds have longer fleeces than others, and the roughest mountain wool is used for carpets and tweeds. The fine Cheviot wool gives woollens (Cheviot tweeds) and the soft short wool of the Welsh mountain sheep is worked up into non-shrinking flannels. The Herdwicks have the roughest of English wools, and give material for carpets ; crossing with the Shetland greatly improves this wool.

The Shetland wool is the long, silky, fine wool generally associated with Shetland shawls. It is sometimes dyed by native vegetable dyes obtained from lichens, but nowadays dye stuffs are imported. The wool industry of these Islands has declined somewhat. For many centuries a close dyed cloth known as wadmel was one of the chief productions, but this fabric is no longer made. Flannel cloth is a domestic industry ; the soft and elastic Shetland tweeds, which make excellent suits for sportsmen, have a market beyond the Islands. The fells of the Shetland sheep are dyed for mats, or sometimes tanned with a native plant and made into the waterproof cloth used by the Shetland fishermen, and the women for field labour.

The home clip of our annual wool production [1] is about 91 million pounds, of which about 26 million come from Scotland and 65 million from South Britain. Its great excellence in special respects still makes it in demand abroad and about 60 per cent of the annual clip is exported. Great Britain is about eighth on the list of wool-exporting countries.

The reader is referred to the Economic Geographies for the main factors concerning the British Cloth-Making

[1] Average for 1921–5.

Industry. We shall merely give a few particulars of two or three cloths of special repute.

The making of plaid was a very anciently established domestic industry derived from the smaller fleeces of the Scottish Highland wool. The first plaid was white in colour, but the subsequent addition of black produced a " chequered " cloth, and finally the plaid became a glorious mixture of colours,[1] so that while different tribes or clans had special colours and patterns to distinguish them, a king or a chief disported seven colours (the law forbidding more), the inferior nobility four, and the peasantry one or two, plain or chequered. A man's status was therefore known by his colours.

The cloth to-day called " tweed " began life as a twill, pronounced, and on one occasion at least spelt, "tweel". The story goes that in 1830 the clerk in a " twill " factory wrote to a London cloth merchant using the phonetic spelling, but his handwriting being rather illegible, the word was read as *tweed*, and a reply sent in which the cloth was so named. The novels of Sir Walter Scott were just then bringing renown to the Tweed Basin, and the twill makers, grasping the splendour of this advertisement, changed the name of the cloth forthwith. The centres of this tweed manufacture are at Galashiels and Hawick, but there are also tweed cloth mills at Peebles, Selkirk and other towns in the Tweed Valley. To-day the wool for its production is mainly imported, and its continued manufacture is due to " industrial inertia ". Yet it seems fitting that Tweed cloth should be made in its " name " district, and perhaps the inherited skill displayed in its manufacture may be regarded as a local resource, apart from the fact that the inhabitants of the valley must have *some* industry.

The wool of the Scotch Blackface provides for the

[1] Held by *some* to have originated in Joseph's coat !

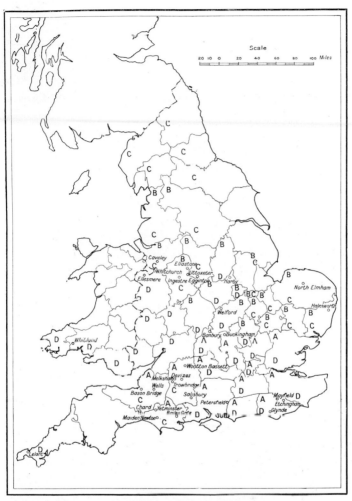

## LONDON'S MILK SUPPLY

London's milk supplies are (1) Direct and (2) Depot. In (1) producers send their milk direct to the purchasers. In (2) they supply large collecting depots owned by the purchaser, usually a large wholesaler, who bulks the milk and sends it to his customers. Of the total Direct Supplies, counties marked A together furnish about 24 per cent., those marked B about 6 per cent. Of Depot Supplies about 42 per cent. comes from counties marked C and 28 per cent. from D. The names on the map indicate the United Dairies' County Creameries. Lelant has a butter-making factory and is not concerned with the liquid milk trade.

carpet and Scotch bonnet making at Kilmarnock, Ayrshire.

The manufacture of flannels in South Wales dates from the middle of the nineteenth century, when a number of hand-loom weavers settled in the valleys of the Teiffi and Towy. Blankets and fine flannels are still a domestic industry in the neighbourhood of spinning mills, though there are some up-to-date factories. The wool of the local mountain sheep, harsh and kempy, is not suitable but is used for the manufacture of bed rugs. The heavier flannels are made into shirtings for the colliers to wear in the mines.

Another product obtained from sheep's wool is lanoline, used in the preparation of toilet soaps. For this the wool is washed and treated with ammonia.

Our leather industry is of great antiquity. It provides for saddles and other horse equipment, boots, shoes, and bags. Its establishment in England coincides with the great belt of damp cattle pasture extending through the Midlands, and including the basins of the Great Ouse and Nen. In addition to access to supplies of hides and skins, the tanning industry would be near oak woods, in order to obtain the necessary gallic acid.

The establishment of an industry so essentially connected with transport would be at market towns, where people needing harness would congregate, the bulk of the marketable commodities being moved, in those days of bad roads, on the local navigable river. In this way Northampton in the fertile Nen basin became a natural centre for the leather goods trade, and still manufactures boots and shoes. Norwich is another natural focus in a rich and early developed agricultural region, which, in spite of the import of raw material, has still flourishing tanneries based on the home product.

There are additional leather centres of ancient and present repute in Lincolnshire. The oak forests of Central England have also helped the tanning and boot industry of Leicester, on the River Soar. Further south-west there was an early domestic glove making industry in the Cotswolds, which still lingers alongside the factory industry at Chipping Norton, etc. Gloves are also made at Taunton in Somerset. The cattle of Ayrshire provided for an ancient industry in shoes (at Kilmarnock, Maybole, etc.).

What wool has been to the sheep milk is to the cattle industry, and it has the advantage of being preferred *fresh*, so that imports of liquid milk are never likely to be of great magnitude. The dairy shorthorn, Devon and Red Polled cows give large quantities of milk, whereas the milk of the Channel Islands' breeds has more fat and is deeper in colour. These latter head the list for richness of milk, after which come the Devons, Shorthorn, Ayrshire, and Kerry. Though our beef breeds are pre-eminent throughout the world, our dairy breeds are outclassed for heavy milking and the transmission of milking capacity.

The great expansion of our dairy industry dates from the rinderpest havoc of 1865. London milk sellers were forced to seek ex-local milk, and many butter farmers of Oxfordshire were induced to supply them. Later, the valleys of the Thames, Evenlode and Kennet gave their contribution, and now " London milk " is collected from very far afield.

The milk of the British dairy herd comes upon the market as " liquid " or fresh, or is worked up into some better keeping commodity. Where transport facilities are inefficient or absent, the farms may utilize their surplus milk for home-made butter or cheese ; where collection from farm to farm is easy, though the region as a whole is rather inaccessible, a central factory may deal with the local milk in mass for production of butter or cheese.  Such factories have been established in Somerset, Devon, Cornwall, Pembroke, and Carmarthen. The former butter trade in Buckinghamshire has been almost ruined by the condensed milk factories at Ayles- bury.  On the other hand, some counties are changing from the production of butter or cheese, or even meat, to milk production, because increased railway and road facilities (especially the motor lorry) can give them a constant and quick market.  The advantage in this milk trade, especially to the small holder, is the quick return, albeit in relatively small amounts.  It has been computed that about one-tenth of the yield of English milk is fed to livestock, about three-quarters consumed as milk, and about one-sixth converted into cream, butter, and cheese.  The great bulk of it comes from the grasslands, and the summer supply is in excess of the winter.  The winter smaller production increases the price, but a farmer keeping sufficient cows to meet the winter needs of his clientèle will have a summer surplus, of which he makes butter or cheese rather than sell the milk at a loss.  Other things being equal, grass- fed cows give better milk than do cows fed in some other way.  Though milk is produced in every county of Great Britain, our dairying districts lie in three distinct regions—South-west Scotland, with Ayrshire as centre and the Ayrshire cow as chief agency ;  a belt across the English Midlands from Lancashire and Cheshire to the West Riding of Yorkshire ;  and the southern counties, from Essex to South Wales, feeding London.  Most of the milk of the first of these regions is sold fresh to the towns of Scotland and North England, and is some- times sent to London.  About 15 per cent of the regional milk is made into cheese, this district being the only

o

cheese-making district in Scotland.   The careful Scotch dairying includes a regular testing of the milk, a procedure which greatly helps the foreign trade in livestock.   The milk of the second region finds a ready sale among the industrial populations here largely congregated in towns surrounded by country upon which are raised the local supplies.   This belt is responsible for the great cheeses associated with the names of Cheshire, Caerphilly, Wensleydale, Stilton, etc., and the regional cow is the dairy shorthorn.   The third great milk region satisfies a considerable local demand as well as the London market.   The enormous summer surplus is worked up into the Cheddar, Caerphilly, and other cheeses.

Up to the sixteenth century " white meat " (milk, butter, cheese, eggs) was the staple food for all classes in the country districts, and the cheeses were differentiated according to place of manufacture.   Tusser regarded Banbury as the best, though admitted that some preferred the Cheshire cheese.

The varieties of cheese manufactured in Great Britain to-day may be classified as hard, lightly pressed, or soft.   Cheddar, Cheshire, Caerphilly belong to the first category and are made both on cheese farms and in factories.   The second category includes the Stilton, Wensleydale, and Dorset cheeses, produced mainly on cheese farms, the factory process not giving such good quality ; possibly the farm cheese makers possess " trade secrets " and inherited skill derived from generations of cheese-making ancestors.   The soft cheeses are of creamy texture, the intention being to compete with the French and Swiss soft cheeses, but as yet the competition is not very serious.   The well-known St. Ivel [1] is a soft cheese.   The United Dairies Limited

[1] From the old spelling of Yeovil, on the River Yeo.

produce the soft English " Petite Suisse " ; the same Company has a factory for making Stilton Cheese.

The Cheddar, Cheshire, Stilton (Leicester), Gloucester, Derby, and Lancashire cheeses are of world repute ; Scotch Cheddar and Dunlop are well-known Ayrshire varieties.  Caerphilly, a variety of Cheshire no longer made at Caerphilly, is highly popular with the South Wales miners ; Stilton and its Wensleydale variety are blue-veined cheeses.  The better grade cheeses are of their best quality when made of the summer milk, and the character of the pasture and nature of the soil are sometimes of the highest importance in obtaining cheese of a particular make, while sometimes the importance lies more particularly in the process.  The difficulty of securing skilful dairymaids accounts for the decline of cheese-making in South Wales.

Cheshire cheese is mainly produced from the milk of cows reared upon the keuper marl and lias grass pastures of north Shropshire, and the red sandstone grass pastures of Cheshire.  Some is also made in Lancashire, North Wales and Somerset.  The popularity due to its taste is increased from the farmer's point of view by the fact that a gallon of milk produces a pound of cheese, leaving in addition much whey for pig feeding.  Its excellencies have caused Cheshire to become the chief cheese making county in England, and the cow population of South Cheshire is denser than anywhere else in Great Britain.  The Shropshire industry was instituted by a small colony of Cheshire cheese makers who settled round Oswestry.  The towns of Lancashire and the Potteries provide a great market for this cheese.  The farms of this great dairy district are small, and their cheeses are made by women.  To keep up the high quality, the chief cheese makers have combined into a federation for standardizing the product, and their trade-mark

C.C.C. (Choice Cheshire Cheese) is inscribed upon their produce.

Cheddar cheese, considered the best of British cheeses, depends greatly for its good qualities upon the breed of cattle and process of manufacture. It can be made wherever the soil is of medium quality, and the herbage short and sweet, the ideal soil being one resting on limestone. It was made in Somerset, Gloucester, and elsewhere by the time of the Stuarts, and as a well-reputed and giant Gloucester cheese it often took two men to lift it when uncut. At the end of the eighteenth century Londoners knew it as " double Gloucester " on account of its size, but a variety made in Warwickshire was decidedly inferior, owing to the less perfect management of the dairies. This cheese, of wax-like texture, was being produced in Somerset, Wiltshire, Berkshire, and the counties of Oxford, Worcester, Lincoln, Derby, Stafford, and even York. Not until 1856, when Joseph Harding produced a definite formula, was the cheese standardized, and the preservation of its good qualities ensured. It received the name of Cheddar in the nineteenth century, because the visitors to the well-known gorge and caves were regaled upon it in the neighbouring village of Cheddar. It is one of the chief products of the dairy farming in the Plain of Somerset, and Somerset, Gloucestershire and Wiltshire may be regarded as its present home. As in Cheshire, the cheese farmers of Somerset have combined to form the English Cheddar Cheese Making Federation for grading the farmhouse cheeses and sending them to market with the Society's stamp of quality. Cheddar cheese is now made in large quantities in Ayrshire, coming into the market as Scotch Cheddar, and competing with the native or Dunlop cheese.

The Wiltshire cheeses now retaining this name are of

three kinds, though all are made of partly skimmed milk. The North Wilts cheese, small and truckle-shaped, is a very good variety ; the Fours, or flat cheeses, in many respects similar to the double Gloucesters, owe their name to the fact that four of them go to the hundred-weight. The third kind is a white cheese 2 inches thick resembling the Caerphilly, a cheap cheese sold chiefly in Wales.

The Stilton cheese is to Leicestershire what the Cheshire and Cheddar are to their respective home regions. Originating in Leicestershire, it can be made in any district, though not much true Stilton is produced outside the county. It was being made in Leicestershire and South Derbyshire in the eighteenth century. The story goes that in the old coaching days a certain Mrs. Paulet of Wymondham, Melton, Leicestershire, made this cheese upon her farm and placed it for sale with a relative who kept the Bell Inn by the turnpike on the Great North Road at Stilton, in Huntingdon. Visitors to the inn tasted and liked the cheese so much that they bought it—for 2s. 6d. a pound. The Bell Inn became famous for this cheese, which in due course was known as "Stilton". In 1903 a co-operative factory for making it was opened at Scalford, near Melton Mowbray, an attempt of the Leicestershire farmers to compete with factory-made cheese.

The Wensleydale cheese has been made on traditional lines for centuries in the dales of north-west Yorkshire. It has been described as " badly shaped, finished, and bandaged ". Of the Liberton and Cotherstone varieties, the first, when well made, is said to equal good Stilton.

Among other cheeses of more local reputation is the Lancashire with its distinctive flavour, and the Derbyshire cheese. This latter, once a farm cheese, is now the product of the milk of the Derbyshire uplands, which

is sold to cheese manufacturers, one of whom will deal
with the milk of fifty or sixty farms.  It is an early
maturing cheese, large and flat, with texture resembling
the Cheddar.

The milk of ewes long provided domestic cheeses on
all sheep farms.  Ewe-milk cheese was once regarded as
a great dainty, but had passed out of favour by the end
of the eighteenth century, though even in 1798 a certain
amount was made from " Cheviot " milk.  It is made
in Britain to-day only on special occasions.

When cows are not fed entirely on grass, unless the
milk can be sold fresh, it may be better to make butter
than cheese.  Butter making in England is not as
prosperous an industry as it was, and though much is
made upon farms for family use, the popular taste of our
cheaper markets is rather for Danish butter, of good
quality but cheap, though cheap " Empire butter " is
now well in the running.  Small farms inaccessible to
liquid milk markets still produce butter, our most extensive butter areas being Somerset, Devon, Cornwall, the
low lying parts of Wales and the Lake District, Wigtownshire and the Scottish south coast lands.  A long standing butter industry in West Oxfordshire still sends a
great deal to Birmingham.[1]

The making of butter is not a popular use for the milk
because 2½ gallons are needed to produce 1 lb. of butter
for sale at 1s. 6d. per lb.  There is little demand for the
skim milk, though it can be used for feeding calves and
pigs.  On well-equipped farms the fat removed from
the whole milk in the process of butter making is replaced
by a cheaper fat obtained from boiled linseed jelly, cod-

---

[1] Oxfordshire formerly produced much butter, but such farms
as supplied London during the 1865 and following crisis were
later unable to resume their ancient butter making owing to the
deterioration of their machinery through long disuse.

liver oil, etc., and added to the separated milk for calf rearing. Butter making is chiefly a home industry, but there are some factories.

Our cream production is small compared with the foreign product. Our chief cream areas are Westmorland, Devon, and Cornwall, though of course it is made elsewhere. The butter and cream of the considerable dairy farming of Cornwall are expressions of the fact that this county of good forage crops and rich breeds of milch cattle is inaccessible to big liquid milk markets. Where possible, the milk is supplied to local factories— Nestlé's have a collecting station at Lostwithiel. But the greater part of the cream is produced upon the individual farms. The trade is seasonal and coincides with the fresh fruit season. The remainder, after removal of the cream, has a high feeding value.

We have now to consider a product of the pastoral industry, whose former importance is by no means extinguished. The use of dung for enriching the ground for the furtherance of agricultural operations was very early recognized. I have tried to show elsewhere [1] how the traditional belief in the unhealing feud between pastoralists and agriculturists is more legendary than real, inasmuch as agriculturists not keeping livestock have generally welcomed gladly the flocks and herds of the more purely pastoral peoples. The dung of animals is rich in compounds of nitrogen, potassium, and phosphorus, and the bacteria always found in it break up the compounds into substances which feed the plant. Fermentation of cow dung generates some heat.

Farmyard manure containing much straw and litter reduces the tenacity and plastic quality in clays, making them easier to work. By adding humus and binding the grains together, it reduces without destroying the

[1] Vide *Water and Grass.*

porosity of light soils.  Poor clay land carrying grass
or arable improves greatly by heavy folding in summer
or dry weather, when sheep can feed on concentrates
and green crops *brought* to them, the dung derived from
this feeding being pure addition to the soil.  Farmyard
manure permits the profitable fattening of cattle in spite
of the expensive feeding and the small excess of the
selling price of the finished product over the price of the
original store.  The value of the dung varies with the
food consumed.  When cattle are fed on cake, meal,
hay, nitrogenous foods, and a small amount of straw,
the resulting manure is richer than that obtained from
store cattle and dry cows.  In the Norfolk four-course
rotation the soil is often prepared for wheat by the farmyard manure arising from the use of the straw and the
haulms of the corn crop as litter and cattle food.  Growing animals are less valuable for manure than mature
ones, since less food is ejected, more being required for
the process of growth.

The dung of the sheep is cold and does not ferment
and so retains its valuable qualities longer than the warm
dungs.  It also contains more nitrogen.  When sheep
eat turnips in the field about seven-eighths of the fertiliz-
ing ingredients of the turnips are returned to the soil.
There is an Italian proverb to the effect that sheep are
the best dung-cart, and the labour of bringing the dung
from the farmyard and forking it over the field is saved
where sheep have been properly hurdled.  In the Norfolk four-course rotation light soils are manured mainly
by the sheep feeding off roots in the autumn, winter,
and early spring and, to a lesser degree, catch crops
in autumn and spring.

The close nibbling of sheep tends to make the plants
spread sideways rather than upwards, and the eating
down of coarse and poor weeds gives the high-grade

grass a better chance, especially if the sheep have
additional food.   In Scotland, where less hill sheep are
being kept than formerly, an increased mortality and
decreased fertility of the ewes has been ascribed to
poverty of the pasture due to the deficiency in the
natural manuring.   The presence of sheep upon a light
soil helps to ameliorate it in a manner unconnected with
the dung since the fine and even treading of the little feet
of the sheep does much to press it firmly together and
give it coherence.   This manuring and treading value
of the sheep has justly earned for it the epithet of
" golden hoof ".

CHAPTER XVII

## THE HISTORIC LEGACY

LARGE-SCALE sheep farming was introduced into Britain by the monks, especially those of the Cistercian Order. Kelso Abbey possessed 7,000 sheep, probably Cheviots ; the monks of Furness Abbey set up Herdwick " sheep farms " in the twelfth century, and the Cistercian monastery founded in the valley of the Teiffi about 1164 possessed the most extensive sheep farm in Wales. The wool of the sheep reared by the ecclesiastical houses was always of good repute and became the basis of much wealth, which was spent lavishly in erecting beautiful buildings such as the Abbeys of Jedburgh and Melrose, certain abbeys of Yorkshire and elsewhere. To the monks also we owe the beginnings of our woollen industry.

As opposed to the peaceful influence of the monks may be placed the more stirring deeds of the great lay landowners, striving to avenge family feuds, snatch pieces of territory, or fill up with vigorous action their otherwise empty days. On the Border especially fury ran high, and found practical expression in forceful change of ownership of flocks and herds. Border raids are of very ancient standing. One of the reasons for the construction of the earthwork known as Offa's Dyke appears to have been to delay Welsh marauders returning from a successful cattle drive, thus giving their owners a chance to overtake and recover the stolen cattle. On the Scotch-English Border raids were a feature almost down to the Union, and in a single such foray nearly 200 towns, churches, peel towers, etc., might be burnt down and over 10,000 cattle and sheep driven off by the raiding party (1544).

The Scotch Highlanders, having no national rage to satisfy, took refuge in clan quarrels, and the Highlanders were adepts in detecting the trails of hurriedly driven cattle. Where the trail died out the law assumed the local chief to be the thief, and demanded restitution. When a raid was successful the chief and clan divided the booty in the proportion of one to two.

Even earlier than 1603 there was an extensive cattle trade in the Scotch Highlands ; marts were sent from Skye to Glasgow by sea or to the mainland by ferry for fattening on the good lowlands of the South or Moray Firth. This trade afforded opportunity for sheep and cattle lifting on a large scale. In the Spey Valley cattle thieving went on down to 1745, and the yearly value of stolen horses, cows, sheep and goats in the Highlands was assessed at £5,000, apart from £2,000 or more disbursed in unsuccessful attempts to recover them, and a further £47,000 in precautions and bribes to prevent theft, and payment of blackmail. At one time the east coast lairds gladly subsidized Highland lairds to maintain watches in the Upper Spey Valley and elsewhere, down whose glens passed the wild Highlanders of the West upon their periodic sprees (spreaghs) into the Moray lands. These sprees took place in the autumn when the marts, now in good condition, were being driven to concentration points—an excellent opportunity for reivers.

The Jacobite rising of 1745 showed up the difficulties of moving large bodies of troops in Scotland, and resulted in much good road making to meet similar emergencies should they arise in the future. The new routes opened up the Highlands for a trade with England in livestock at a time when attention was being given to the production of good meat, and an industrial population able to afford it was steadily increasing.  Thus was originated the great industry in West Highlanders and Galloways, etc., passing a store period in their romantic glens, and later traversing the new roads towards their finishing pastures.  It should also be noticed that the new facilities for transport aided in putting down organized cattle raiding.

Perhaps the next excitement in the Highlands was that provided by what has come to be known as evictions and clearings.  The new trade with England, the high price paid for British wool, seemed to point to an extended sheep industry wherein large-scale sheep farmers stood to make great profits.  Throughout the eighteenth century the keeping of improved breeds of sheep in large flocks had been spreading northward from the Border. Highland estates, forfeited after the Jacobite rising, became the property of southern sheep farmers, while the lairds still remaining in their districts were also quick to recognize the advantage of the new husbandry. The small farmer, almost without capital to buy sheep, could no longer count on the head of his clan for either help, home, or grazing rights, and labour in the new industries, or emigration oversea, appeared to be his only resource.

Actually much of the " top lands " was unsuitable for cattle, and in the old days they had been eaten over by sheep, but by numbers too small to make full use of them. At first sight it would seem that the Blackface might have invaded these heights without prejudice to the traditional exploitation, but the highlands are very bleak in winter, and to utilize the full summer resources winter quarters had to be found for the young sheep and lambs on the lower grounds in the glens or straths.  In

consequence much land formerly allotted to the cattle
in winter had now to be reserved for sheep owned, not
by small farmers, but by their great landlords. The
small farmer not only lost his holding, but could not
even find work locally, since hill sheep do not require
much supervision and the shepherds employed were
southerners. From this period dated the decline of
population in the Scottish Highlands.

The Sutherland evictions left peculiarly bitter re-
membrances. They began in Ross and Sutherland
towards the end of the eighteenth century. The heather
moors of these counties make good grazing for the Blackface, while the cotton and other grasses of less bleak
positions give a good bite for winter and spring. In
1792 a determined but abortive attempt was made to
drive out the alien sheep, whose invasion was greatly
extended a few years later. Nearly all Sutherland belonged in her own right to an infant Countess. When
grown up she married the Marquis of Stafford, later
created Duke of Sutherland. Between 1811 and 1820
the estate became a vast sheep farm, 15,000 persons
being evicted for this purpose. The former inhabitants
were removed to a fringe of smallholdings on the coast,
and became the crofters of these northern realms. By
1889 similar evictions had been worked on more than
two million acres in Scotland, much arable land, as well
as uncultivated heaths, becoming a " wilderness for sheep
farming ".

From very early times there were extensive drives of
livestock from one part of the country to another, but
with the establishment of the great beef breeds and the
new means of supplying winter food and fattening forage,
this movement became considerably augmented. Stu-
pendous journeys from Aberdeen and even farther north
to the English lowlands for finishing, with a final walk

to London for slaughter, were part of the annual routine, as were also lengthy journeys from south and west.

Some of the transit routes were very ancient; they lay upon the Downs or across open moors and had been trodden out by the droves of the men of the later Stone Age and succeeding peoples. The oldest of these British routes and trackways occur on the Downs of south and south-east England. They pass near or through earth-work encampments; the best surviving, the so-called "ridgeways", lie along the crest of the hills, and the "camps", giving shelter for the night and water for man and beasts, are often a fair day's march apart.

Though fallen into disrepair and often obliterated for long stretches, names such as "Ox Drove", "Welsh Way" (in various forms) denote their former site and use. An Ox Drove, catering for Somerset cattle, can be traced from Exeter to London as Welsh Way, Welsh Lane, etc., catered for those of Wales and the cattle collected by the Welsh drovers en route. The Ridge-ways of Berkshire and Wiltshire made part of a still existing route taking Anglesey cattle to Kent. Other ridgeways and early routes still used are the Bath and Downs Ways for Gloucester flocks, travelling eastward, and the Icknield Way. When fenced to prevent stray-ing these Ways are the best of all routes for travelling stock. The permanence of the track is due often to the properties of chalk, which is not too hard to receive an impression from continual transit, nor too soft to lose it when such transit ceases. Many of these Ways were abandoned and deteriorated during the later centuries, but were revived simultaneously with the increased movement of livestock, when their use could save the drovers the expenses of the turnpike toll.

Where the ancient Ways lay on chalk or greensand, or some other light soil, they would be open all the year

round, but where they crossed the clay vales of the
Midlands the depth of the winter mud made it necessary
for graziers to sell their stock in early autumn.

The small and hardy old Welsh breeds of cattle could
well stand the fatigues of long marches to their finishing
grounds. During the sixteenth and seventeenth centuries the Welsh cattle dealer, or porthmon, was of great
repute. In late spring or early summer he scoured the
country for store cattle for disposal in Warwick,
Gloucester, London, and Kent. He also executed
personal commissions in far-off places for his clientèle.
There was always much mortality among the sheep and
cattle while on the march ; when murrain was very
prevalent the head of a defunct beast raised upon a pole
warned the drovers to make a détour cutting out the
infected district.

The annual export of cattle from Scotland became so
remunerative that the leading chiefs of the West paid
their mails and duties through its profits. The concentration of cattle for sale to a dealer or drover was known
as a *tryst*. In the eighteenth century McCombie of
Tillyfour went in person to Caithness, Sutherland, Skye,
and the Isles, buying cattle which he took in large droves
to Tillyfour, where they were sold by public roup for
fattening on the local lowlands (" low " Aberdeen), or
driven farther to the southern markets and fairs, especially in Leicestershire. At one of the October Falkirk
Trysts this same great cattle trader and breeder had
1,500 cattle, 900 of which were Highlanders, and the rest
Aberdeen beasts. There yearly went out from Dumfries
25,000–30,000 head of cattle for finishing in Leicester,
Northamptonshire, or upon the salt marshes of the
eastern counties.

The trysts were fed by farmers or local cattle markets,
for hardly a parish existed without its livestock market

within walking distance. The August Tryst at Falkirk dealt with 5,000–7,000 cattle, mainly West Highlanders from Skye and the mainland, destined for the English Border counties or Midlands, or for gentlemen's parks round London. Much later a great cattle fair was established at Kelso, at which shorthorns from Yorkshire and Cumberland were bought for local fattening.

Wherever their place of origin, the animals required shoeing, which was done at concentration points and halting places. Need for shoeing was more frequent in autumn than in spring, with its finer weather. Tipping varied from one to eight hoofs per animal. After being at grass for a few weeks the feet of store cattle became hardened, and from the end of May to August cattle were marched along at the rate of 10 to 14 miles a day. When on the great roads their food consisted mainly of what they could pick up from wayside or hedge. Large flocks of sheep also journeyed far southward from northern pastures, and London was additionally supplied from the south. On April 21st an enormous drive of fat sheep set out for London from the Romney Marshes, and until the institution of railway transport large numbers of sheep, bought at the great Weyhill sheep fair in October, began their 50 to 60 miles journey to London, walking at the rate of about 8 miles a day. As the ewes were in lamb at this period, a horse and cart accompanied them to convey such lambs as were born en route.

The growing badness of the existing roads for wheeled and other traffic ultimately led to an arrangement by means of which large stretches of the main roads were kept in repair by the towns or villages along the route. Money for expenses was extracted from the people using the road, who were admitted into the various stretches by the turning of a pivoted bar or pike normally closing

the road.   The first toll gates on the Great North Road
were erected some time after 1663 at Wadesmill, Caxton,
and at Stilton ;   by the end of the next century turnpikes
were very common.   The toll for cattle was 5*d*. a score,
and for sheep or lambs ½*d*. per score.   After 1750 about
100,000 head of cattle and 750,000 sheep went annually
to Smithfield, while Scotland alone sent 100,000 cattle
to England each year.   Onward from 1799 the cow-
keepers about London kept few cows other than shorthorns of the Yorkshire breed ;   they were bought in
Durham, Yorkshire, and Leicester, and also went south
to Northamptonshire and Bedfordshire, where they were
bought for the London district by the cow-keepers, or
dealers who sold them subsequently.   As befitted its
pioneer experiments in agriculture, the great object of
the Norfolk husbandry was to " fatten bullocks " (a
loose term, denoting all sorts of cattle) for Smithfield,
etc., the said bullocks being mainly Galloways and West
Highlanders.   The farmers of east Norfolk bought them
at the end of summer at such fairs as St. Faith's, on
Bullocks Hill, near Norwich, to be stall-fed on local
turnips during winter.

The size of the drive depended on circumstances.
Drives were known to extend, three or four animals
deep, for a mile.   One drover might have charge of
5,000–6,000 lambs, or 300–400 cattle.

The vexing tolls led the drover to find cheaper lines
of route, and broad drove roads developed, providing
grazing and camping space for large companies of cattle.
Such roads can still be traced in parts of England and
especially in Scotland.   Country lanes were likewise
used, increasing the length of the journey, but giving
softer going and a better free feed than the higher grade
roads.

Circumstances often drove flocks and herds along the

P

highways to some special market or because no other
road was available, and the trampling and stamping of
the animals helped to soften the surface and produce
holes which cart wheels turned into long ruts.

Among drovers the Irish were held to be incomparable
for making cattle " go sweetly ", though some very good
drovers came from the Western Isles. The ideal drover
walked two or three feet ahead of his procession to set
the pace, the cattle following two or three abreast.
When seized by panic the cattle would run for miles,
and the unexpected tinkling of a brook was sufficient to
set them off. About twelve hours a day was the average
drive, with a two to three hours' break at noon. A
journey might occupy several weeks. The mortality
*en route* was often very great. McCombie, whose homing
route lay across the River Spey, then unbridged, lost
seventeen Caithness runts in one night.

From its earliest beginnings the pastoral industry has
afforded a means of payment. Cattle or sheep settled
many of the feudal dues. The feudal heriot compelled
the heirs, on the death of a farmer, to give the best farm
beast to the lord of the manor, while the Church also
extracted a cow from the bereaved family. The Abbey
lands of Cupar gave the tenants all its manure in payment of service. The customs levied on exports were
a different type of due, benefiting the country as a
whole, as money spent on administration. In the fourteenth century wool was Scotland's greatest export, and
the custom duty on wool and wool-fells totalled three
times the amount of that of the previous century. In
England the wool duty paid the greater part of Richard
I's ransom. In 1288 livestock belonging to Scots in
Yorkshire was confiscated to pay a debt owed by the
King of Scotland.

Down to the end of the eighteenth century the shepherd received his wages partly, or even entirely, in kind —so many lambs at lambing time, keep for his little flock with the rest (the shepherd's ewes *never* miscarried), the price of the wool of his own sheep at shearing time, and the sale of his own ewes' lambs. One advantage of this method of payment was the encouragement it gave to the shepherd to do his best for the flock with which his own was mingled.

In feudal times over much of England part of the rent was paid in corvée and manure. Plaiding, skins, and hides sometimes settled the rent in the Islands of Western Scotland ; the Shetlanders anciently paid their scat or land tax to their overlords, the Kings of Denmark, by means of the fabric called wadmel. In the Scottish Highlands the sub-tenants frequently settled rent or back payments by rearing or wintering young stock belonging to their landlords. When rents were heavy the autumn sale of black cattle to south-country drovers generally paid it in full. Highland cattle provided a maiden's dowry, a similar practice being long in vogue in parts of Britain.

In Celtic and Saxon days cattle were used as a form of currency, the value of one man being equivalent to that of 100 cows. The Saxon kings later fixed one cow as being worth three ounces of silver. Henry I and the early Plantagenets accepted the taxes in terms of sheep and the Church rates of their time were sometimes assessed in money or the equivalent in rams. The 1*d.* wage to which women shearers or shepsters were entitled could be substituted by the wambelocks, or loose locks under the sheep's belly.

The institution of " cow charities " were often of great boon to a village ; pious men would bequeath money for purchase, upkeep and replenishment of oxen for use of the parish poor, either free or for a nominal charge.

Such charities have now died out or altered their scope.

The methods of marketing the products of our industry have played a great part in our national life. In early times each little district was self-sufficing, the produce being used at home by the producers, but from the fourteenth century onwards fairs were established to deal with the farm surplus. The developing cloth trade delighted the housewife with visions of other fabrics besides the family homespun and the fairs became marts for livestock, wool, cloth, as well as other commodities. Among fairs the purely livestock fair is the oldest, but in time wool and cloth were added, merchants from abroad visiting them to buy our wool and sell their own cloth.

Our fairs were closely related to festivities, since hearts might be reckoned happy after something had been sold at a profit, or some new possession acquired. The hiring of temporary premises and the right to sell meant the exaction of rent, tolls, and dues. Frequently some local lord or ecclesiastical dignitary was " governor " of the fair, and gladly received these tolls. Since fairs were without meaning unless people were free to attend them, they were generally held upon the holidays afforded by the Festivals of the Church, and even at the present time and especially in the north of England a number of ancient fairs are held on the day of the local patron saint. Originating through the general lack of easy routes of transport, and being unable to supply a region with ex-local commodities more than two or three times a year, fairs naturally declined when the institution of railways made it possible for constant supplies to be sent to a district at any time. There were, of course, other causes contributing to the decline of our fairs; thus the great

Cloth Fair of St. Bartholomew, London, dealt very largely with the sale of cloth from the Low Countries, but by the end of the fifteenth century British cloth was being sold at this fair, and when English cloth became as good as that of Bruges, Ghent, and Ypres the special reason for the St. Bartholomew Fair had ceased to operate.

British fairs lingered on as more purely livestock, cheese, or pleasure fairs, frequently combining the sale of other things with a certain amount of amusement. The livestock fairs have still a vogue, since for various reasons the movement of livestock for sale is often quite conveniently and much more cheaply effected on the hoof. But the increasing use of the motor car is a recent and a rather devastating blow to the continuance of this fair since buyers of large numbers of animals need not wait till sheep and cattle are concentrated at the fair grounds, but can in a few hours inspect personally the stock of many farms.

Space can be found here only for a brief mention of but two or three out of the very great number of fairs in existence or extinct in Great Britain. The Stourbridge Fair, on the Stour, near Cambridge, is an ancient fair at which the wool packs of Old England were purchased by Italian merchants, who brought hither foreign cloths and other commodities in exchange. By the eighteenth century we had long been weaving our own wool and the Fair dealt with vast quantities of Yorkshire cloth.

The Falkirk Tryst and the Inverness Character Market were the most important of their several kinds in Scotland. The Tryst was a great feature of the livestock trade of the eighteenth to nineteenth centuries and concentrated northern and southern dealers, the former generally to sell, the latter generally to buy, though there was some trade in the reverse direction. This Tryst was held in August, September, and October. The earliest Tryst dealt principally with West Highland cattle and has already been described. The September Tryst dealt with the hill sheep from the north of Scotland, Scotch Blackfaces and Cheviots in equal numbers. This was mainly a wedder (= wether) market and the best Cheviots went to Cumberland and the best Blackfaces to Ayrshire, Wigtownshire, Edinburgh and West Lothian. Some cattle were bought for early beef, mainly West Highlanders. The October Falkirk dealt with draft ewes and Highland stores bought as " straw treaders ". The Falkirk was also supplied with calves from both Yorkshire and Lancashire ; they were bought by feeders and graziers of Forfar and Fife. The calves were generally dehorned to make them less troublesome in yards.

Among the still existing ancient livestock fairs of Scotland may be mentioned those at Lockerbie and Edinburgh in August. Others are held at Crieff, Kelso, Dalkeith, Hawick, etc. In the eighteenth century some 20,000–30,000 head of cattle were sold for export to England for winter fattening. The once famous Hawick Ram Sale declined considerably in the latter part of the nineteenth century, most of its business being now done by commission agents.

The Inverness Character Market was largely concerned with the disposal of wool, and was held annually for three days in the summer. Certain " plane stones ", still to be seen, were the site of the market.

Until 1816 the Sutherland and Caithness sheep farmers disposing of vast quantities of wool supplied their regular customers year by year as well as roving wool staplers with no special connection. A certain Patrick Sellar, the agent for the Sutherland Association, meditated upon the advantages of a centre for buyers and sellers alike and on February 27th, 1817, a meeting of the clans was held at Inverness to consider the matter.   The outcome was the establishment of the Character Market for the disposal of the wool of Northern Scotland and the Islands.   The purchasers were the cloth manufacturers of Huddersfield, Wakefield, Halifax, Burnley, Aberdeen, and Elgin.   Neither sheep nor fleeces were seen at the market ; the wool to be disposed of was " cried " on the stone, the reputation or character of the flocks and their owners being guarantee of their value.   The buyers of the previous year obtained the first offer.

Sheep fairs are still common in England, though shorn of their former splendour.   The Ram Fair at Keswick takes place in October and Herdwicks are the main sheep involved.   The Herdwick draft ewes are still sold at a number of fairs anciently established in the Lake District (Hawkshead, Eskdale, Ambleside, Kendal, Windermere, etc.).   In the South of England 20,000–100,000 head of Hampshires are sold at the summer and autumn fairs.   The Sheep Fair at East Ilsley (Berkshire Downs) dates from the reign of Henry III, and is one of the most ancient and important sheep fairs in England. The chief fair is held on August 1st, 20,000 sheep being penned on each side of the village street.   The Weyhill Fair is almost equally famous and at one time dealt also in dress and home fabrics.   The Yarnbury Fair (October 4th) held on Salisbury Plain, the Tan Hill Fair (August 6th) close to the Ridgeway, are both easily reached by sheep travelling over the Chalk Downs.   The Marlborough Sheep Fair, held in August, is attended by 20,000 sheep and lambs, chiefly of the Hampshire Down breed ; these popular sheep are also seen at the sheep fairs of Overton, Wilton, Salisbury, as well as Weyhill and East Ilsley.   One of the largest sheep gatherings in Sussex is at Lewes (September 21st).   The Oxford Great

Ram Fairs are declining, partly because of the decline in the number of Oxford Down Sheep, though this sheep figures considerably at the September Great Ram Sale at Kelso.   Wool and fleece are still sold at the Blandford and Dorchester Wool Fairs.   Other noted livestock fairs are held at Newcastle-on-Tyne (Cow Hill), Hereford, Lincoln, Barnet, etc.

On any one occasion the Market is of less importance than the Fair ; it is generally held at intervals of one to four weeks, or bi-weekly.   Anciently markets and fairs were under similar protection, the market dues going to a lay or ecclesiastical overlord.   There are about 1,300 licensed livestock markets in Britain, the predominant type being found mostly in the small country towns, whose centres they occupy.   The livestock is housed in pens of temporary or permanent construction, or tied to railings, or herded in groups.   The business transacted is small, and confined to about a dozen buyers, one or two of whom are local farmers, and the rest belong to an " outside ring ", whose members have combined to avoid competition.   The periodic auction sales of to-day have done much to destroy the glamour of the old live-stock market.   The large markets can be distinguished as those established either in areas of considerable surplus or in areas of considerable consumption.[1]   The first are markets mainly for export, the second entirely for import.   The Preston market is an example of the first kind.   Huge, practically all under cover, it can pen large numbers of animals which, while waiting sale, are housed in separate stalls and kept in good condition. There are two markets each week, the one dealing with dairy stock, the other with fat stock, with special sales at intervals for store and breeding stock.   Hundreds of

[1] F. J. Prewett (1926), *The Marketing of Farm Produce*, Part I, Livestock.

cattle and pigs come from the Fylde district for disposal, via Preston, for the industrial population of the east and south. The dairy cattle come from Cumberland and are sold to the local milk farmers.

The Caledonian Market in London is a large " consumption " market. It has lost much of its former glory and even on market days the number of empty pens is very great. Its decline is due to the sale by auction, now so much in vogue, and the increasing propensity for dealers and butchers to do their business directly with one another, the latter slaughtering the animals themselves or paying the cost at some slaughter centre.

The modern auction mart is generally held near the station of some big town ; the farm supplying it may be distant, but the farmer can send his livestock thither in a lorry and by putting on a reserve price, save himself, if he so desire, from personal attendance.

The City Corporation owns four of the markets connected with the London livestock and meat trade. The Central Market at Smithfield serves mainly the London area. Its Charter goes back to Edward III ; it can display at once over 60,000 sides of beef and has cold storage facilities adjoining. The Metropolitan Cattle Market and Abattoir, Islington, holds a livestock sale twice a week and also possesses the chief slaughter-house in London. It has hanging capacity for 5,000 animals and most of its meat is sold at Smithfield.

The present system of marketing is the result of gradual growth. Generally speaking, agricultural produce is brought up by the country dealer who sells it to a wholesaler, who disposes of it to the shopkeeper, who retails it to his customer. These three middlemen standing between producer and customer may be much increased, but the middleman plays a useful part in the scheme. He assembles the products of many farms, grades, sorts, and possibly stores for a while his purchases, makes the transport arrangements, and may even engage in some preliminary " working up ", such as slaughtering.

Something has already been said about livestock shows. They are very numerous and it would be tedious to list them here. A complete catalogue is issued every spring and is supplied free of charge by the publishers of *The Farmer and Stock Breeder*, Lenmore House, Norfolk Street, Strand, London, W.C.2.

## CHAPTER XVIII
## THE SOCIAL LEGACY

DURING the Mediæval period most of the annual episodes connected with British husbandry were regulated by " Saints Days ".

At Candlemas [1] lambing began and the Keeper of the Lambs took up his annual functions and certain water meadows were laid up for hay for the use of separate individuals. On the following day, the Festival of St. Blaize, the patron saint of woolcombers,[2] there was much merrymaking, involving processions and ceremonies, in wool cloth-making districts. St. Valentine's Day [3] was a great occasion for sowing beans, while St. Gregory's Day [4] was another and more usual occasion for laying up the water meadows for hay. On Lady Day [5] open-field farmers put their ewes upon low-lying pasture till folding time ; some tenancies ended at this date. The annual service of fold-soke (folding of villagers' sheep on the lord's holding) began on Hokeday.[6] Many tenants folded their sheep and sometimes their cattle on the lord's demesne from this date till Martinmas,[7] which period also marked the end of the proper grazing season. Hoketide [8] marked the beginning of the barley sowing,

[1] Feb. 2nd.
[2] St. Blaize appears to have been Bishop of Sebasti in Armenia, martyred at the time of the Licinian persecutions. The fact that he was torn to pieces by iron combs may account for his connection with woolcombing.
[3] Feb. 14th.      [4] March 12th.      [5] March 25th.
[6] 1st Tuesday after Easter.      [7] Nov. 11th.
[8] 3rd Tuesday after Easter.

which generally ended at Pentecost.[1]   Helenmas [2] was a great date for the sale of fat lambs, St. John's Day [3] came at the end of the early summer feed and set the time for selling off fattened old and feeble ewes ; and the Keeper of the Lambs finished his yearly term of office. On Lammas Day [4] the autumn rye sowing began and in some districts ewes were not milked after this date to give them time to be fattened for the Michaelmas [5] sale; common rights, as apart from the strip cultivation, began in the arable fields, the stubble and aftermath providing sustenance for livestock pastured in common, the hay harvest on the water meadows was now taken up.[6]   On the Day of the Nativity of the Virgin Mary [7] all ewe milking ceased, so that the animals could get into good condition for the winter.   The agricultural year ended at Michaelmas, at which date aged ewes, whose worn teeth would no longer permit them to nibble the scanty winter food on the sheep walks,[8] bought in August for fattening were now killed and eaten or " cured " for consumption later on ; this was also the more usual date for ending tenancies.   On St. Luke's Day [9] draught oxen were removed from field labour and stalled for winter.   At Hallowtide there was much slaughter of " fat crones and such old things " and feasting for the peasantry, this general feasting actually extending from Michaelmas to Hallowmas,[10] upon which latter date the sowing of the winter rye was concluded.   Martinmas[11] brought a great slaughter of beasts in good condition after the summer feed.   Most of such cattle were preserved as " hung beef ".   From

[1] Whitsunday.          [2] May 3rd.          [3] June 24th.
[4] Aug. 12th.               [5] Sept. 29th.
[6] In some remote districts fields alongside a stream are still known as Lammas.
[7] Sept. 8th.              [8] Crones.              [9] Oct. 18th.
[10] Nov. 1st.                      [11] Nov. 11th.

Christmas [1] to the Epiphany [2] the shepherd was entitled
to fold his lord's sheep on his own land and so get the
manure. Other similarly described dates are connected
with the various livestock fairs and special pastoral
duties.

The ecclesiastical flavour of these dates cannot be
denied, but they point less to an edifying piety than to
a reason found by experience to be advantageous for
the various pastoral operations ; in those days there
were none of the modern methods for reminding men of
the passing of the months, and the Saints' Days, in
volving celebration of some rite at Holy Church, were
dates which the priests would never allow their charges
to overlook.

We shall now consider the place of the pastoral industry in literature, both serious and recreative. In
the first case there are prose works definitely intended
as agricultural treatises, and poetical works, where the
intention is really similar, but the method that of con-
cealing the pill by the jam. Prominent among such
works of Tudor England is Fitzherbert's *Husbandry*
(1523), urging that sheep should be well fed ; Tusser's
*Hundred* (later *Five Hundred*) *Good Points of Husbandry*
(1557), describing in verse ideal methods and times of
planting and sowing, with particular reference to forage
and pasture crops ; Googe's *Four Books of Husbandry*
(1577), in which he decries English cheeses as the worst
of all cheeses ; William Harrison's *Description of Britain*
(*c.* 1580), extolling British breeds of cattle and sheep as
being second to none ; and Leonard Mascall's *Book of
Cattle* (1596). Hartlib edited a remarkable amount of
agricultural information in his *Legacy of Husbandry*
(1651), to which Sir Richard Weston contributed sound
instruction upon the use of sainfoin, lucerne, clover, etc.,

[1] Dec. 25th.                                    [2] Jan. 6th.

as forage crops.   Other writers were Gervase Markham,
Professor Richard Bradley, who urged farmers to adopt
large-scale arable farming with a full rotation in place
of fallow (1726), John Dyer, whose didactic poem *The
Fleece* bespeaks the trend of his interest, Marshall, whose
various *Rural Economies* (*c.* 1796) deal with the new
breeds of sheep and cattle, Arthur Young, in whose
*Travels* is to be found much advice, some of it good,
upon contemporaneous farming methods, Daniel Defoe,
who also described the rearing of livestock in Britain
as practised in his day, William Youatt, whose compre-
hensive work, first published in the opening years of the
nineteenth century, has been enlarged and brought up
to date (1908), and James Caird.[1]   An early reference to
the Cloth Industry appears in Chaucer's *Wife of Bath*,
whose homespun was declared superior to the Ypres and
Ghent cloth.

The more recreative works deal with a different aspect
of the pastoral industry.   With few exceptions the life
of the shepherd is described as to be desired above that
of the " king on his throne ".   In general this shepherd
of the poets would appear to lie about all day in the
shade of hedge or tree, or swathed in hay up to
the chin,[2] and protected from sun and wind, while the
lambs, safe in embowered enclosures, gambolled the
hours away.[3]  When not dozing the shepherd played upon
his pipe of reed or corn stem.[4]  A shepherd might spend
his entire day in chat or song, whether reclining at ease
in the pasture field or jogging home,[5] to the boundless
admiration of his wife,[6] who possibly thus secured immunity for the deficiencies of her commissariat.   Some-

[1] For more recent writers see the Bibliography at the end.
[2] Barclay's *Eclogues*, sixteenth century.
[3] Phineas Fletcher (1582–1650).
[4] Chaucer (*c.* 1340–1400).     [5] William Warner (temp. Eliz.).
[6] Robert Green (temp. Eliz.).

times shepherdesses accompanied the shepherds and occupied themselves during the hours of general concert by virtuous knitting,[1] though there were interludes of passionate wooing.[2]  Utter contentment was a common characteristic.  The shepherd considered that he alone of created beings led a merry life ;[3] his days and nights were more tranquil than those of the cattle he grazed.[4] His sheep followed him as subjects follow their king.[3] He could lie and " snort " his fill at nights whereas care caused kings to be wakeful.[9] Sheep hooks were infinitely preferable to sceptres.[5] His innocency equalled that of his sheep.[6] His recreations at home were telling tales and playing bowls,[4] but fair days and holidays enabled him to display his muscular prowess in sight of the lasses, when he stood to win a sheep or a sheep's hook.[7] The crowning of the Shepherds' Queen and the election of the King and Queen of the Sheep Shearing were others among his simple pleasures.[4] His equipment was a long cloak, sheep crook, sling, script, tar-box, pipe or flute, and dogs.  When he went courting he was apt to offer the best wool, his whole equipment and shepherds' *tales* to his lady.[8]

Even in Scotland the shepherd's life was delightful,[10] for after putting their flocks to pasture, groups of shepherds reclined upon the ploughed strips, regaling themselves with " any sort of milk ", or, having rested sufficiently, " sat up " and told tales or danced country dances.  Shepherd literature of this description arose

---

[1] William Browne (1591–1643).
[2] Christopher Marlowe(1564–93).
[3] Michael Drayton (1563–1631).
[4] William Warner (temp. Elizabeth).
[5] J Heywood (c. 1497–1580).          [6] Phineas Fletcher.
[7] George Withers (1588–1667), Wm. Browne.
[8] Nicholas Breton.          [9] Robert Green.
[10] " Complaynt of Scotland ", *ante* 1603.

probably from the desire to emulate the classical tradition, and had little kinship with the life of the shepherd
of the manor village.   On occasions, however, the poets
did illustrate with local references, though large-scale
rather than manor farming seems indicated.

Legends and folk-lore connected with the pastoral
industry lingered for a long time in our wilder districts.
The results of the seeding-time, harvest operations and
soil fertility consequent upon the folding and herding of domestic stock were early ascribed to the miracles
of the saints.   Among cattle the dun cow was regarded
with peculiar favour, and credited on occasion with
having relieved the thirst of communities during drought
by giving unlimited stores of milk.[1]   Such legends probably originated in some real superiority of milk yield
when compared with that of cows of another colour.
The more purely fairy or nursery story also comes
into this category.   The little brown hare in the Manx
nursery tale is connected with goblins who skulk among
the sheep.   The Black Sheep may be both good and
bad, and in connection with the good black sheep it
may be noted that as late as 1887 serving maids hired
at a fair stipulated for a little wool in addition to
their wages to furnish what to-day we should call the
" bottom drawer ", and which was often their only marriage portion.   Until comparatively recently stockings
for females were white, black, or grey, the latter a
mixture of black and white.   The Welsh mountain sheep
often begat black-haired lambs and a few black ewes
were kept here, as elsewhere, for household wool.   This
short account gives meaning, perhaps, to the nursery
rhyme concerning the Black Sheep, in which it will
be remembered the *maid* was not forgotten !   At the
same time the black sheep was somewhat of a freak

[1] *Vide* the Dun Cow of Warwick and Grimsargh, near Preston.

and rather apart from the rest of the flock, hence the use of the term to denote someone unlike the rest of the family, an originality to-day regarded as derogatory. However, a verse popular in the sixteenth-century enclosure troubles gives another origin for the opprobrium attached to black sheep: " Till then I thought the proverb did but jest which said a black sheep was a biting beast."

Our old friends Jack and Jill apparently lived somewhere on the slopes of the South Downs during the Celtic or earlier period, when they adventured up the hill to the local dew-pond, only to make an untimely descent down the rough chalk tracks or slippery grass-covered slopes. Taffy the Welshman, surely most famous of the cattle-lifters, pined among the sheep of his mountains for less mutton and more beef—a yearning not unknown in our own times, and his thieving propensities must be put down to geographical environment rather than innate criminality.

The curious jingles by which some shepherds still count their flocks, appear on first hearing mere childish babbling, but actually they represent a carefully devised enumeration. In one method the sheep are counted up to a score, after which the counting is begun again, the total being given as so many scores and the odd numbers. In another method the counting is still in scores, but the scores are built up of couples instead of units. Below is an example of each type : Yain, tain, eddero, peddero, pitto, tayter, later, overro, coverro, dix, yain-dix, tain-dix, eddero-dix, peddero-dix, bumpitt, yain-a-bumpitt, tain-a-bumpitt, eddero-a-bumpitt, peddero-a-bumpitt, jiggit (Nidderdale numbering), and the second . onetherum, twotherum, cockerum, qutherum, setherum, shatterum, wineberry, wigtail, tarrydiddle, den (Sussex).

The first of these countings exists with slight variations in many parts of our remoter districts,[1] and like the
others is believed to represent the Welsh numerals which
doubtless have been inherited from the Celtic-speaking
inhabitants of Wales.  It is held that these jingles, found
to-day in districts long occupied by the Celts, represent
the original countings of their shepherds as they took
the flocks past the tally house at night after the day's
pasturing in the open.  These shepherds would be the
subject race during the Anglo-Saxon dominance, thus
perpetuating their rural traditions.  The Sussex score
shows much alien influence, but appears to indicate that
the sheep passed the tally post " two by two ".

The very ancient songs still sung by the Hebrides
women during their spinning, weaving, and cloth-
making operations (like those in the Scottish Highlands
long ago) also appear to have some " counting " quality.

Our industry furnishes many examples of proverbs
and sayings.  The black sheep and the golden hoof of
the sheep have already been mentioned.  The saying
" to go scot-free " is a variant of " to go scat free "
and originally referred to the scathold of the Shetland
Islands,[2] to go scot-free was to avoid paying the scat
or land tax to the Danish rulers.  The origin of the
allied phrase " to avoid paying one's scot or scat " is
obvious.  " To go on a spree " may also have its pastoral origin.

Among party or personal designations may be in-
stanced Whig and spinster.  The " legend " goes that a
certain powerful political group bestowed the epithet of
" tories " upon their opponents from a word meaning

[1] Professor Skeat.    He gives a Lincoln score thus : Yan, tan,
tethera, pethera, pimp, sethera, lethera, hovera, covera, dik,
yan-a-dik, tan-a-dik, tethera-dik, pethera-dik, bumpit, yan-a-
bumpit, tan-a-bumpit, tethera-bumpit, pethera-bumpit, figgit.

[2] See page 144.

" give me ", whereupon the " tories " in retaliation
dubbed the opposition party " whig " or sour milk !
In early days the spinning of wool was a domestic
operation undertaken by the females of the household
irrespective of rank or state ;  they were therefore the
spinsters.  The present significance of the word spinster
in England as describing unmarried women may be due
to the earlier phases of the Industrial Revolution when
the new inventions connected with weaving necessitated
a great increase of thread, for which purpose hosts of
women and children were employed.  The now obsolete
shepster designated a female shearer of the thirteenth
century.  The verbs to dock, to cull, to ear-mark, to
fleece, have been derived from certain operations effected
on lambs and sheep.  The words crones, crony, stinted,
unstinted, explain themselves.

The pastoral industry has provided a goodly proportion of surnames.  Runt, Cow, Duncalfe, Bullock,
Bull, Steer, Veal, probably represent families whose
ancestors specialized in some particular branch of the
cattle industry ;  Cowman and Penman are surnames
with an official flavour, Hook and Crook have an ovine
tang, as has also the Christian name of Sheila, a little
grey sheep.  The influence of the sheep industry is
further seen in Shearer, Lambkin, Fairlamb, Hogg (a
name frequently met with in Northumberland), Lamb,
Sheepshanks, Shepherd, Wedderburn (a stream for washing wedders) and Collie (the sheep dog).  Fletcher
(Flesher), Butcher, and Slaughter probably belong to
either branch.  Hayward recalls the officer supervising
the hay allotment, and Croft a small farmer on the
northern sea-board or in the Highlands of Scotland.
The surnames Fuller, Dyer, Draper, refer to the processes of manufacture and sale of cloth.[1]

[1] List compiled from personal knowledge.

Not less fruitful has been the heritage of place names. The Saxon Stead or Sted marked a peaceful step in the colonization.  They are the sites of a dwelling or farm, and Elmstead, Plumstead, Stansted, Nurstead are some examples taken from the villages of north-west Kent.  The common fields of the manorial system may come in here as the flocks and herds both benefited and were benefited by the agriculture.  Northend, Southend, Kingfield, Longfield, Lammasfield, etc., are again examples from north-west Kent, while many towns possess smaller divisions such as Eastfield (as at Eltham), Southfield, etc.  The commons too, upon which the sheep and cattle grazed, have left their names all over the country.  From north-west Kent also may be cited Woolwich, Kidbrooke, Plumstead, Bostall, Chislehurst and Eltham commons.

Some obvious derivations occur with such place names as Cow Hill at Grimsargh and Newcastle-on-Tyne, the latter Cow Hill being the scene of a long established cattle market.  The various wicks of Canvey and Foulness Islands, Essex, are place names derived from one form of the dairy industry.  Canvey formerly fed 4,000 sheep of delicate flavour, milked by boys, the milk being converted into ewe-milk cheese in the wiches or dairy sheds.[1]

In Britain, as elsewhere, the pastoral industry has always given opportunity for the performance of sacrificial rites.  Even as late as the seventeenth century the sacrifice of a bull was reported at Dingwall.  In the Isle of Man, Beltane, the opening of the summer half of the year, was inaugurated with the burning of two sheep.[2]  Under the Druid régime white bulls were sacrificed when the mistletoe was cut from the oak tree.

[1] Camden, *Britannica.*
[2] Professor Rhys, *Manx Folk Lore and Superstitions.*

Until the middle of the nineteenth century a calf was sacrificed in order to remove horse and cow diseases and a lamb burnt alive to avert an evil spell cast on a flock.[1]  Not very long ago every Whit Sunday a lamb was drawn in a garlanded cart about the parish of Kingsteignton, Devon, killed and roasted whole the following Tuesday and then sold cheaply to the local poor.  This custom originated in pagan days and is said to have been a thank-offering for a miraculous spring that appeared during a drought ; scientists believe this spring to be still in existence underground.  Other pagan ceremonies now degenerated to a species of horseplay are as follows :  May Day on Dartmoor is celebrated thus :  before dawn, young men catch a ram on the moor, tie it to a certain granite pillar, kill and roast it and at midday scramble for the slices.  Formerly on Exmoor an aged wether was shorn and its tail greased, after which it was let loose on the hills.  It was then pursued by young men and became the property of whoever could hold it one minute by the tail.  In Oxford girls with tied hands chased a fat lamb, its captor becoming the Lady of the Lamb ;  the animal was afterwards partly boiled, roasted, and baked, and then consumed by the " Lady " and her companions.[2]

Celtic religious ceremonies involving the lighting of beacons are believed to have taken place at Tan (= Fire) Hill.  It has been suggested, however, that these beacons were lit to guide the drovers who came over the Downs to the Tan Hill Fair, held in the ancient British encampment.

Among superstitions may be mentioned the following : Until recently Durham butchers marked the flesh of slaughtered animals with a cross or a fern leaf, a " super-

[1] Hunt, *Romance and Drolls of the West of England*.
[2] Folklore, 1886.

stition " which may have arisen from the practice of putting aside the " priest's " portion.  The bellowing of a cow at an unreasonable hour is held to indicate a death in the family ; a funeral custom observed in some districts down to the nineteenth century was to make a cow follow the coffin to the churchyard and may have originated as payment to the priest for saying the funeral mass and preaching the funeral sermon.  A legend possibly connected with the belief in the transmigration of souls comes from Woolwich, where an ox, after tolling a church bell, took on human guise.

There are more superstitions connected with milk and butter than with any other farm produce, possibly because milk is one of the most important of foods. In 1878 the Lancashire peasantry still believed the Milky Way (Cows' Lane) to be the heavenward path traversed by departed souls.  An old Celtic superstition well known in Scotland and Ireland is to the effect that witches in the form of hares run among the herds on their way to be milked and steal the liquid by sucking the cows' teats.  Even in the early years of the nineteenth century a Scotch witch in the form of a hare was " frequently seen " milking cows.[1]  There were a number of charms for preventing theft of milk ; hairs from a cow's tail were plaited with straw and tied round the cow's horns or hung on the door of her shed. Sometimes shepherds went to the fields at night to murmur charms and frighten away werewolves and witches who sucked the cows' milk.[2]  In the Shetland Islands it was until recently the custom during Christmas week to exorcise the trows or evil spirits, who have power over the cattle for this one week of the year.  Formerly farmers with a grudge against a neighbour got a " wise woman " to put a spell on this neighbour's cows in order

[1] Athenæum, 1846.           [2] Michael Drayton.

to lessen the milk yield. One way to safeguard milk and butter from witchcraft was to wash the dairy utensils with water taken from the meeting-place of *three* streams. Spilling milk is considered unlucky, but the flick of a cow's tail in the face during the milking operation is a sign of money coming. If milk be borrowed it should be paid back in kind, not coin. Butter is the luckiest of all presents.

The use of charms is but another form of superstition. Manx people sometimes carry about the " lucky bone " of a sheep to be used at crossroads where the route is doubtful ; the bone is flung forward and its owner takes the road to which the hammer end points. A now obsolete practice was to put a lock of wool in the shepherd's coffin in order to notify the recording angel on Judgment Day that his duties had excluded him from the otherwise compulsory attendance at church. In Northamptonshire, Devon, and Sussex it is still believed that cramp can be prevented by wearing near the skin the palate of a sheep or lamb ; at night this " cramp bone " should be put under the pillow.

In some form or other cows' milk has long been recognized as a useful lotion or medicine. Queen Elizabeth is said to have washed her face in milk in order to keep it pale, while the famous Diane de Poitiers is said to have kept her youthful loveliness to an advanced age by the use of milk baths. A milk wash was and is still advocated as softening the complexion after the hardening effects of outdoor games, wind, and sunburn. In the seventeenth century Dr. Sampson Jones and others were prescribing red cows' milk for consumptives ; a cure for whooping cough was to lie down in the early morning where the sheep had lain at night, and not so long ago people suffering from lung trouble were urged to follow the plough, or sleep over a cow-

house.   Country folks in Berkshire still maintain that
the smell of sheep cures diseases, and that it is healthy
to work near a fold, and in Somerset the cure is extended
to consumption.   When King Edward VII had typhoid
fever, wiseacres of Northampton suggested wrapping him
in a fell still warm after its removal from a sheep !

## CHAPTER XIX

## THE PERSONNEL

FOR our purpose the personnel of the pastoral industry will be taken to include both the animals and their attendants. Not much need be said about cattle. The Aberdeen-Angus is well known as a " fierce beast ", but cows in general are singularly docile, though on occasion they may show signs of excessive self-esteem.[1] Cows possess weather sense—they run round when rain is at hand and sit down in the field in fine weather. When they crowd together, their heads in the direction of the wind, a storm is at hand. Male calves not required for the breeding stock are castrated when very young.

The semi-wild life lived by many sheep has enabled them to retain their ancient characteristics to a greater degree than is the case of cattle. One of these characteristics is the flocking instinct, which makes them easily collected together, though the Romney Marsh sheep do not feed in bunches and the Scotch Blackface and other mountain sheep move apart when feeding. The follow-my-leader instinct has been turned to account by man ; for example, sheep likely to stray to the home region after removal remain contentedly in their new quarters if the flock leader is debarred from flight by having two legs tied together. The love of mountain sheep for the native heaf makes draft ewes from Scotland taken to Cumberland try to return to their old home before lambing, and indeed they have sometimes

[1] Frances Pitt, *Animal Intelligence.*

235

managed a secret return, though involving a 50–60 mile journey. Where mountain sheep, such as the Blackfaces, are accustomed to transhume to the low country for winter, the older ewes have been known to start off for the wintering ground on the first fall of snow, and if fine weather set in before the date of their customary return, such sheep tend to stray to their summer grazings.

Shepherds have long availed themselves of the " weather forecast " issued by their mountain flocks. If being down hill they begin to mount, fine weather is expected ; sheep prefer to sleep on the heights, but if in winter they are found descending, the shepherd knows a storm is brewing. When sheep jump about with tails up, rain will fall very shortly. If they gambol, fight, or retire to shelter, the weather is about to change. Old sheep are said to eat greedily before a storm and sparingly before a thaw. Whent hey leave their high pastures and bleat a great deal during the evening and night very severe weather is at hand.

Whether the sheep should be led (a pace thus being set) or driven (so that the shepherd can the more easily keep his eye on his charges) is a moot point. The Palestine shepherd led his flocks ; Drayton makes Melanthus lead his sheep " like a king at the head of an army." Migrating Romney Marsh sheep are often led along the unfamiliar country roads and many of the Sussex shepherds lead their flocks over the Downs. But in general sheep in England are *driven*, though the system adopted depends largely upon the training the sheep dog has received.

Sheep are usually regarded as very foolish animals, but they do show a certain amount of sense. Some of them allow starlings to settle on their backs, the birds picking the ticks out of the wool. In hill country they

graze along little terraces—eating round the hill rather
than over ; probably they have discovered this method
is less fatiguing.

During their short lives sheep go through some or all
of the following operations :—castration and docking,
washing, shearing, ruing, dipping, ear-marking and keeling.  Castration is performed on young male lambs from
2 to 4 weeks old ; the operation is simple and generally
done by the shepherd.  Immediately afterwards the
lambs should have their tails cut.  This docking, which
is also applied to ewe lambs, is essential where sheep
are to be folded, to avoid picking up dirt.  Different
breeds have their own style and length of tail.  The
tails of the partly arable Down breeds are cut off completely, but some breeds retain a length of 2 inches, and
mountain sheep are docked only to a very small extent,
the tail being the natural protection of the back.  The
object of washing is to improve the quality of the wool
and make it bright and clean, a special necessity when
the animal is to be shorn later and the wool sold, or
when the animal is itself to be sold and should look its
best.  Where flocks are small " tub " washing may
suffice and can be done at home, otherwise the sheep
are driven out to some pool or stretch of river near by.
The pool washing has the advantage that the water
retains the fatty acids of the natural yelk (or yolk)
washed from the wool, which act as a soap, the water
thus becoming soapier the more sheep that go into the
pool.  Convenient dimensions for a pool are 25 yards
by 5, and 6 feet deep at one end, the water shallowing
towards the other.  The sheep are thrown in or made
to jump in, and after swimming across they scramble
out on to a prepared gravel beach.  Sometimes the
jump faces a temporary lamb fold, so that the ewes
dash into the water and cross it eagerly in order to

get to their young ones.   Where the flocks are very large
it may be safer to substitute an artificial bath for the
river, the passage of the sheep being controlled by two
pairs of washers.   Sometimes when the sheep are being
prepared for sale the keeper combs the fleece as they
swim in the water.

A running stream makes a good bath, but as the yelk
cannot collect in adequate quantities to cleanse the
wool, two men stand in tubs placed in the water, the
one washing the sheep as they are passed one by one
into the water and the other handing them on to a man
on the bank.   The sheep are then led into a temporary
pen where they remain till all are washed.   The washing
usually takes place about the beginning of June and the
shearing, or clipping, as it is called in the North, about
ten days later, a delay which allows the yelk to reform
on the wool.   If wool, when cut from the living animal,
has not a certain proportion of this natural oil, it mats
together and is difficult to manipulate.   Sheep, however, are not always washed before shearing.

The sheep of to-day are shorn either by man or
machinery.   In Wales the shearing is still done largely
by hand.   Many Welsh farmers own several thousands
of sheep and the work is performed by gangs of shearers
who migrate from one farm to another and labour, on
an average, sixteen hours a day.   The mountain sheep
have to be collected in one place from distances ranging
over many miles ;  the assembling is the work of the
sheep dogs, who drive them into the pens placed, if
possible, near a mountain stream.   The shearers remove
the entire fleece, after which the animal is branded,
dipped and turned out to graze.   These methods are
also operative in Galloway.   On lowland farms the
shearing is done in sheds near the farm.   The lowland
sheep are sheared at the beginning and the mountain

at the end of June, since sheep can endure their fleece
longer on the cooler heights.

The Sussex shearing in the " good old days " was a
highly organized affair.   The shearing gang, numbering
some 30 members, was named from a locality within
their radius of work, such as the Portslade Company.
The gang elected two of their number to serve as
Captain and Lieutenant for the season.   The Captain
arranged the dates of the different shearings, the purchase of new shears, the allotment of pay for the hands.
The season for any one gang lasted about two weeks.
Matters were settled at a meeting known as " White
Ram Night ", sometimes held at the Captain's cottage,
but more usually at some inn, each member contributing
1s. towards the expenses of the entertainment.   On
payment of the same fee shepherds and others interested
might also join the gathering.

During fine weather the shearing was done out of
doors, the sheep or its wool passing through the hands
of the catcher, shearer, winder, tar-boy, shepherd, etc.
The shepherd drove his sheep into a pen before daybreak,
close penning being less harmful to sheep who have not
fed copiously ; ewes and lambs were penned separately.
The shearing began about 7 a.m.   The catcher took the
animals from the pen as required ; after the fleeces had
been removed the winder—often an old ex-shearer—
rolled them up.   When the skin was pricked by the
point of the shears the tar-boy put a dab of tar on the
wound—to-day a pinch of lime is used instead.   When
the shearing was over the gang repaired to the farm barn
or coach-house for supper, a festival that might last
several hours, and was graced by the presence of the farm
servants, and at times by the members of the family.
The shearing season closed with a final meeting at the
inn—Black Ram Night—at the same attendance charge

as before. The Captain paid out the money earned and collected the price from those who had purchased new shears. Shearings of this character were in vogue down to the middle of the nineteenth century.

On hill farms the farmer who provided the gang with the best food and whisky was considered the best " stockman ". On such farms the gang was (and is) often made up of shearers culled from the several farms of the district. In the lowlands and on the Downs the shearers were generally a hired gang paid by the day or number shorn. The usual price for shearing was 3s. to 5s. per score or 3d. per ewe and 6d. per ram. A good hand could shear 80 hill sheep and 40–60 lowland sheep a day, though sometimes the day's total was very much greater.

After the shearing a " buist " (initial of the owner) or brand mark was put on each sheep. This mark was made originally by an iron stamp dipped in tar or pitch before applying.

It is now unusual to shear lambs before their first winter as they really need their full natural thatch to prevent rain from soaking into their wool. In consequence the number of shearers has been greatly reduced and shearers of to-day bring their own provisions and board themselves outside the farms. When the fleeces are small the fine short lamb wool is the most valuable of its kind ; the finest wool of a sheep is about its throat (Scotch haslock or hawselock). Sheep kept on arable land get their fleeces much dirtier than do hill sheep and " grass " sheep often forego the preliminary washing.

In Sussex and elsewhere much of the shearing is still done by hand, especially on small farms, but mechanically driven shears have become the custom with many " large " farmers, the driving power being supplied by

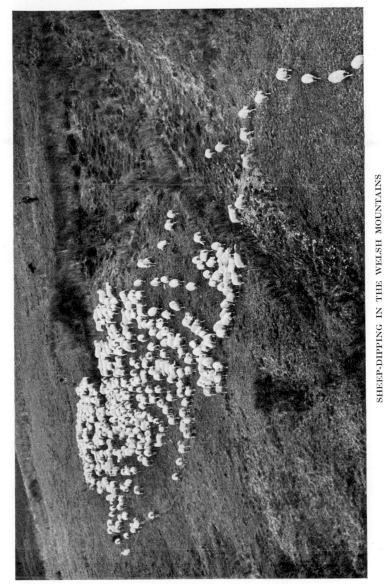

SHEEP-DIPPING IN THE WELSH MOUNTAINS

steam, horse, or water. The experienced hands receive
5s. per score.

In the Shetland Islands the wool is pulled and not
cut off the sheep's back. This process is known as
ruing and is said to assure the fineness of the next crop
of wool, cutting being held to coarsen it. Ruing is not
really barbarous, for the Shetland breeds shed their wool
if it be not removed and it comes away easily without
apparent pain to the sheep.

After the shearing and branding the sheep have now
to be dipped. In all climates sheep are liable to become
infested with parasites, of which the scab insect and
maggots are the most troublesome. For prevention and
cure sheep were formerly smeared with tar or butter,
but for some time it has been the custom to dip them
once or twice a year in a prepared solution, the first
dipping taking place after the shearing, and the second
when the stock has been made up for the winter. A
tub is used for small flocks, but where numbers of sheep
are kept there must be a more expensive construction.
The bath, tub, or box, is filled with the solution to the
required depth and the sheep are lifted in one at a time,
being held so that none of the liquid is swallowed.
The animals remain in the bath for a few minutes, are
taken out, and their wool well wrung.

The operation of ear-marking is of very ancient
origin. A notch was made in an ear of each animal
in order to establish ownership in case of thefts or
straying. To-day ear-marking is reserved as an identification number in the flock which is recorded on a
register giving the necessary details of the sheep's
career, to which reference can be made when required.
The ear-marking is effected by a notch, or a punch, or
a tattoo mark on the ear, or by simple attachment of a
metal tag.

Finally, a sheep may have a keeling mark. On hill farms some days after dipping, and when the stock has been made up for the year, the whole flock is keeled or ruddled, that is, each sheep is marked with a device peculiar to each farm and easily seen at a distance, so that straying sheep, if not far from home, can be returned. These marks, sometimes made with tar, may be black or red ; they are published in a *Shepherds' Guide*.

Something should now be said about those attendants of the flocks popularly designated " sheep dogs ". The Scotch collie, the sheep dog of Northern Britain, is said to surpass all others for intelligence and usefulness as regards work with sheep and cattle. The bob-tailed sheep dog is mainly seen on the English Downs ; it is the old English sheep dog preferred by South Down shepherds, less susceptible to heat than the collie, but also less meek and less intelligent. A mongrel sheep dog derived from a collie cross is also very usual. The name *collie* has an association with a word meaning *black*, originally referring to the attendance of the collie or " black dog " upon the collies or Blackfaced sheep !

The highly trained sheep dog is a model of skill, devotion and obedience, guided by the raised, lowered, or pointing hand of its master, or the modulation of his voice, or whistling. Its labours do not cease from dawn till the sheep are folded at night ; its training is severe, no petting being allowed, since its business is to bark at strangers rather than expect food and caresses from them. It must never be allowed to go a-hunting, and generally the size of the flock it guards makes this diversion impossible. It performs its duty without hesitation ; the shepherd goes to the fold where his sheep are grazing and a nod or a look from him sends the dog running round the boundaries so that no sheep can escape its notice, and by incessantly running backwards and forwards it gradually reduces the circle till all the sheep are massed where desired. When all are collected the dog can pick out any animal the master needs. If the sheep are to be kept in two or three separate groups, the dog can arrange it. Usually working close to the sheep, he barks at their heels if they seem inclined to loiter.

When on the Downs the dog rounds up the sheep by barking, drives them away from green food, holes in wire fencing, open gates, etc., to wherever the shepherd requires them. When going to the fold at night he drives the sheep in the rear to push and crowd those in front, and so gets them through the opening into the hurdled enclosure. The dog also barks off intruders from the flock; where sheep are fed in folds on hay placed in wicker cages the dog goes within the hurdles and barks off such lambs as are trying to steal the hay destined for their elders, not retiring from the enclosure till the meal is finished.

Shepherds have been encouraged to train their sheep dogs by means of competitive " sheep dog trials ". In the north of England great interest has long been taken in the breeding and training of the collie and, acting on the initiative of the Countess of Bective, the Northern Counties' Association for the Improvement of Sheep Dogs was formed in the latter part of the nineteenth century. Working trials, with rewards to owners, were held successively in Cumberland, Westmorland, Lancashire and Yorkshire, and the results seemed to prove that the pure-bred collie excelled the ordinary cross-bred strains.

Sheep-dog Trials, still a feature in the north and in Wales, are confined in the English Midlands and south

R

to Tring and Hyde Park in London.  The trial is conducted somewhat as follows : Three sheep are at large
on a hill some distance away ;  the shepherd whistles
and signals and the dog runs to the sheep, rounds them
up, and drives them through several sets of hurdles,
keeping them all the while together, and finally drives
them into a selected pen.  The shepherd meanwhile
stands a little way from the hurdles, pens, etc., to
guide the dog.  The time of the whole operation is the
main quality of the trial.  Both in Scotland and in Wales
the shepherd's dog may " follow him to church ".  This
was formerly the case in England and the Isle of Man,
where various parishes appointed a " dog whipper " to
keep the animal out of the sacred edifice.  The office of
dog whipper was kept up at Baslow Chapel, Derbyshire,
till the beginning of the nineteenth century ;  at Halli-
well, Yorkshire, the parish beadle was also dog whipper
(1860) and functioned under the name of " Dognoper "
(nope = northern for a knock on the head).  In Scotland and Wales well-behaved dogs were allowed to
remain for the service.

Among the more human personnel of our Industry the
shepherd is particularly prominent.  He is a man whose
life is peculiarly bound up with that of his charges, and
since the sheep of the grasslands and heaths receive
much the same attention wherever their habitat, it will
be convenient to deal with the shepherd as a type,
noting some particular differences only as they occur.

The shepherd is usually a man of sturdy, independent
character, taciturn and slow of speech, illiterate (if
English), but of a deep and simple faith.  His outdoor
life makes him exceptionally healthy, the shepherds'
branch of the community being third on the longevity
list.  He recognizes the beauties of nature as far as he
understands them.  A shepherd has been known to

collect " flint implements " which he will not sell, but
will part with to friends.   He is extraordinarily frugal ;
a shepherd of eighty years declared he had not eaten
more than 6 lb. of butcher's meat during the sixty years
of his marriage.   His outdoor life has made him exceedingly weatherwise.[1]   His outstanding quality is a spirit
of conservatism and a deep reliance on the sufficiencies
of his fathers.   He scorns reform because it emanates
from the new sheep owners who have no " sheep-feeling "
in their bones ;  moreover he knows his own methods
are the only correct ones.   In some Scotch shepherds
the customary, rather unreasoning cocksureness is supported by illustrations drawn from the teaching of the
local dominie, and the native intelligence fostered by
an education denied to the older Southern shepherds
has given the Lammermuir shepherds great reputation
in the hill country of Northumberland and Durham.

The shepherd's devotion to his charges is proverbial ;
he spares himself no trouble in promoting their welfare.
A generation or so ago he began his apprenticeship at
18 years old, on an annual wage of £16 to £25 and his
keep.   When he became a master-shepherd this pay was
increased by the use of a cottage, a small field, a little
meal, and a flock of 80 sheep.   When supplemented by
a braxy victim well sluiced in a stream, his little farm
supplied the entire commissariat for himself and his
family.

The greater part of the shepherd's life is spent in
solitude, especially on the Downlands.  From early
morning till folding time for the whole year he is working for and with his flock, toiling over the hill in atten-

---

[1] This old shepherd of fifty to seventy years' service is fast
disappearing.  He came of generations of shepherd ancestors,
but to-day the young people decline this profession.  The
Downland shepherd, however, still pins his faith to the ancient
traditions.

dance on the sheep, especially when the ground is sticky and rough, setting upright such ewes as may have rolled over, administering remedies to sheep bitten by flies, taking the evening tally, and going forth, if necessary, to seek the strays.

At lambing time he builds a fold near a hay-rick, which supplies food and litter, and lays out rows of coops containing hay for the sheep to draw out and eat.   His hut near by contains his handlamp (once a lanthorn) to enable him to make several rounds a night.   If a ewe dies or cannot feed her baby he gives it a " bottle ", or transfers it to a ewe who has lost her child, first putting the skin of the dead lamb upon the living one in order to deceive the bereaved mother.   After his five o'clock breakfast he lets the ewes out on the hill side while he clears up the pens.   The ewes and lambs basking in the wintry sun are inspected and counted, and on Downland areas the ewes are driven to the dew-ponds and back again.   The shepherd's holiday may be a day in a decade.

When the sheep are entirely " arable " the shepherd's life is, of course, very different.   The Berkshire sheep, for example, spend all their time between hurdles and the shepherd's duties are mainly those of preparing, supplying and allotting the good feed.

The Down flocks are often very large, numbering nearly a thousand.   The pasture rent is low because the great amount of furze and coarse grass adds to the acreage required for the upkeep of a flock, an average allowance being one acre per animal ; the associated arable land is much dearer.   On parts of Salisbury Plain the ewe flock may number 5,000 head, and so large an acreage is necessary that some of the shepherds ride after the sheep on horseback.   The South Down shepherds count their length of service thus : each

seven-year period completes a year of working Sun-
days, and seven such sabbatical years is a creditable
record of service.  Some shepherds can boast for themselves, their fathers and grandfathers eight or even
nine such years' service (fifty-six or sixty-three true
years).

One of the shepherd's quaint customs still surviving
is the method of recording the number of sheep by
notches on tally sticks ; a shepherd's clock, constructed
by placing upright sticks on the arc of a circle, will give
him the time of day by means of the position of the
shadow.

Some shepherds carry on small subsidiary industries ;
a former industry of the South Downs was the snaring
of the beautiful wheatear, a bird once regarded as a great
table delicacy.  In hunting countries the shepherds still
stop up foxes' earths the night before a meet ; the
remuneration is 10s. per fox killed before getting to
earth in the district under their control.

The shepherd's equipment is very simple.  During
Anglo-Saxon times he wore a sheepskin cloak and a tunic
which has survived as the round smock gathered in a
little at the waist and falling a little below the knee.
The smock has survived in Shropshire as the *hamp*,
made of hampen homespun.  In cold weather the shep
herd wore an additional woollen cloak, often replaced
by the military cloak bought cheaply after wars.  The
woollen cloak was originally of one colour and later
on the mixture of the natural black and white known
as Shepherd's Plaid.  In wet weather the cloak was
exchanged for one of unbleached calico brushed with a
preparation of boiled oil and lampblack to make it rain-
proof.  A red handkerchief tied round the neck, a straw
hat in summer, a soft felt chimney pot in winter and tall
laced boots completed the special outdoor wear.  Under

the smock, which was not worn by all shepherds, was a
red and yellow waistcoat covering a coarse blue jacket,
blue worsted stockings, corduroy breeches and trousers.
A large umbrella was carried in case of rain.  The old
outdoor wear has now been replaced almost everywhere
by strong suits of corduroy of various shades, black
bowler hats and stout overcoats, and the size of the
umbrellas has been much reduced.

The pastoral crook, or hook, is still a badge of office.
Besides serving as a walking-stick the shepherd uses
it to catch sheep by the hind legs and lambs by the neck
where it is desirable to remove them from the flock for
inspection, or to set them upright if they have rolled over.
Formerly the crooks made by one Berry, the blacksmith
of Pyecombe on the South Downs, were considered
superior to all others and passed from father to son.
They were constructed of wrought iron, gun barrels, ash,
hazel, and holly wood.  Shepherds' crooks are now
manufactured in the north of England and retailed in
shops.

The shepherd's " bottle " is a little keg or wooden
barrel in which he carries some " cold, thin drink ",
formerly a herbal concoction of dandelion, burnet, nettle
tops, ginger, sugar, etc., now replaced by home-brewed
beer or cider.

The bells worn by the flock leaders were often of
beautiful workmanship and made by the shepherds.
Bells are still worn but their use is declining.  The early
cattle bells were of wood and the sheep bells, at any rate
in Sussex, were of smelted or welded charcoal iron of
ancient local manufacture.  The sound of the bells
recalls the lambs to the ewe flock and helps the shepherd
to locate the sheep after dark, or in a fog, or when
stolen or strayed.

The shepherds of yore put much loving work into

the making of yokes and lockyers. The yoke is a neck ring to which the bell may be attached, while lockyers are pegs for holding the bell strap to the collar and yoke. Both are made of yew, but lockyers are also constructed of sheep's rib bone.

Other former attendants upon the sheep were the looker and the lamber. The looker was really the Romney Marsh shepherd who looked after the sheep. The Romney Marsh lamber attended the ewes at lambing time; his perquisites were the skins of dead lambs, a custom hardly making for skilful " midwifery ". The looker still holds this position; he may be employed by several stock owners simultaneously at the price of 1s. 6d. per score of sheep per year.

The fogger ( = fodderer) is the Wessex term for the farm hand who tends the cows and other cattle and pigs. His territory is the farmyard and the meadow; he knows each of his charges by name.

As we have already seen, the shepherd's year was brightened by certain feasts and festivities. The " Lambs Feast " was one such feast formerly given by the Romney Marsh graziers to the upland farmers bringing back the lambs after the wintering. These farmers and their servants met the Marsh shepherds at some convenient inn *en route* and when the lambs were safely encamped, masters and men indulged in a great dinner, including unlimited drinking. The expensive dinner was paid for by the graziers, who believed it encouraged the winterers to give their best attention to the lambs.

The Shepherds' Meets of the Lake District and the Pennines concluded with much conviviality. The most famous meet to-day is that of Mardale, held in November and attended by many others besides farmers and shepherds; the proceedings are diversified by fox-hunting, hound trails and concerts. The Shepherds'

Meet of November 7th, 1878, at Saltersbrook, Yorkshire, was the occasion for the return of 121 strayed sheep, (*The Globe*, 1878).

The festivities accompanying the shearings are of very ancient origin.   Shears have been found in Roman graves.   The shearings of the Manor Farm and later period were always times of merrymaking, when the farm maidens, attired in their best, waited on the shearers at the final feast presided over by the duly elected King and Queen of the shearers.   This occasion has always been a great one, especially on hill farms where links with life beyond the farmlands were few. Mrs. Gaskell describes such a shearing feast among the Cumberland Hills,[1] and even to-day the ancient glory of sheep-shearing has  not  quite  vanished  from  the remoter districts of Scotland.

The most educational of all shearing displays were the great Holkham and Woburn Sheep Shearings upon the estates of Coke of Holkham and the Duke of Bedford.   To them came visitors from near and far that they might learn from the example of these two great stock breeders both what to do and how to do it.   The Holkham Sheep Shearing assumed a definite character in 1778 and these " clippings " continued until 1821, when they ceased owing to trouble which followed the intrusion of politics into the conversations.   Arthur Young saw " Mr. Coke and the late Duke of Bedford " in shepherds' snods superintending the sheep pens. Other sheep-shearings were notable in their own way. Potton, in Bedfordshire, anciently possessed a great wool trade, and at its sheep-shearing merrymakings, which included a masque and morris dancing, there was personification of St. Blaize, the patron saint of Wool-combers.   This festival, now extinct, was once common

[1] *Household Words*.   Edited by Charles Dickens.

in many of our manufacturing towns. Down to the middle of the nineteenth century Bradford held a Septennial Jubilee on February 3rd in honour of St. Blaize and Jason of Golden Fleece fame; a similar St. Blaize Festival, marked by processions, music, and speeches, used to be held in the cloth-making districts of Essex. The last times such celebrations were kept at Saffron Walden, Colchester and Coggeshall were in 1778, 1782 and 1791 respectively.

The seasonal character of the pastoral industry has given rise to the problem of the " dead season ", especially where livestock requiring much superintendence are removed from the region in winter. The problem has been put very clearly by E. J. Russell [1] in his article " Regional Facts in Agriculture ". Upon the great grasslands of the clay vales that provide so much summer grazing the farmer fills in his winter leisure by hunting and breeding horses, and races, balls, and the general activities of a hunting district help him through this period of ennui. The Welsh store cattle farmer, out of work after the spring or summer sales, finds some outlet for his energies in the National Eisteddfodau. Possibly the singing streams, the murmurous waterfall, and the organ-tones of the air blowing through the valleys have played their part in his musical development.

[1] *The Geographical Teacher*, Spring 1920.

CHAPTER XX

## MODERN DEVELOPMENTS

I T will be useful at this stage to review briefly the
fluctuations of the pastoral industry through the
nineteenth and twentieth centuries. The establishment
of free trade inaugurated a period of very intensive high
farming, which was hardly affected by the bad harvests
of 1848–53, since the industrial population could afford
to pay the raised prices. The effects of the Crimean
and American Wars, by again raising prices, increased
the farmers' prosperity, since the nation, still largely
agricultural, could produce almost all its needs. The
'sixties and 'seventies of the nineteenth century may be
regarded as the golden age of British farming.

The fortunes of our industry were furthered by the
interest taken in it in high places. The Royal Agricultural Society of England was founded in December
1838 with Queen Victoria as patron, and under the
auspices of some of the most wealthy and enlightened
landowners and practical agriculturalists of the day.
Its Committee was soon making arrangements for annual
exhibitions of farm stock and implements. Several
important Cattle Societies, such as the Shorthorn Cattle
Society, came into being and the establishment of Flock
and Herd Books assisted to keep up public interest
and a general standard. The year 1874 inaugurated
more than two decades of deep agricultural depression.
Farm labourers began to demand the higher wages
already accorded to industrial labourers, whose better
standard of living they also wished to emulate, and new

transport developments were opening up new countries and making it possible for them to put agricultural commodities on the British market at a cheaper price than the home country could produce them. In 1875 wheat from the United States of America was finding a cheap market in England and a series of wet harvests began four years later, this time unaccompanied by rising prices, owing to the ever-increasing imports of the United States and, later, Canadian and Australian grain. To the harvest disasters of the wet years was added the decimation of the British sheep owing to liver-fluke. Between 1879 and 1881 about three or four million sheep died of this disease. The small arable farmers, especially tenant farmers, became bankrupt and gave up their farms, which the landlords had to utilize as best they could. One of the most striking results was a species of migration, initiated about 1890, farmers from the west coming south and east down the whole extent of the country. In the wetter lands of the west and north there is and was much cattle raising which had no connection with arable farming based on grain as major crop ; these regions were unaffected by the wet harvests or the heavy imports of grain, and farmers who had managed to save a little capital bought up the derelict farms at low prices and ran them on their own home methods. Hard-working, frugal, family farmers from Cornwall, Devon, and Somerset moved eastwards as far as Oxford and Berkshire and from the Scottish lowlands as far south as Essex ; the new-comers farmed for milk, the family provided unpaid labour and their profits were ensured, since milk is untouched by foreign competition and a market in Greater London and other urban centres was near at hand. The new exploitation did not help the mass of the original farmers, who had neither capital for a new start nor knowledge to carry on successfully an unaccustomed occupation.    Such arable farmers as had saved some capital weathered the storm by farming on a large scale, farming for milk, and working several cheaply purchased derelict farms in addition to their own holding.    The work was hard, but the profits, if small, were sure.    Some of the arable farmers increased their grassland by cutting down their grain land, and reared and fattened livestock with the help of cheap imported grain and oil seed residues.    Such farming reduced labour and also permitted small profits.

After 1896 things began to mend.    As in previous ventures, livestock farming saved the situation ; the production of *meat* was now its object, but even so all was not plain sailing.    For some time past countries overseas had been sending us sheep and cattle to be killed on landing or soon after.    This import did not greatly affect the home prices as the population was growing and the poor conditions of the animals on landing made the meat of inferior quality.    But the introduction of the refrigerator presently allowed the importation of frozen carcases and chilled meat in good condition from our Colonies and the Argentine, so that English meat of inferior quality had now to face the adverse competition of good and cheap overseas supplies. Nevertheless, during this time British farming was steadily on the up grade, helped in some measure by a better knowledge of farming methods gained from agricultural experiments and education.

The World War of 1914–18 had the effect of reclaiming to arable farming much land lately used as pasture, and from 1914 to 1920 farming profits were high in spite of the dearness of farming implements and material.    The end of the War did not see immediately the reduction of arable, though less forage crops were grown and the increased price of " feeding stuffs " and labour adversely affected the arable sheep industry, while the frozen meat in storage at home and abroad at the end of the War so lowered prices that for some time sheep-keeping was definitely unprofitable, and much arable land lost the sheep it has not as yet recovered. But as the cheap grain imports resumed their old course in face of a continued high price of home labour the difficulties of arable farming again became manifest. From 1918 to 1928 nearly 2 million acres of arable land have been allowed to tumble down to pasture, generally of a very indifferent quality. This has been especially the case in the south and west and in the counties of Leicester, Northampton, Surrey, and Sussex,[1] with results already considered. Unfortunately much land in the eastern counties has too little rain or too sandy soil for permanent grass, so that stock-raising which might replace profitably the declining arable cultivation is not possible.

In Cheshire and Lancashire economic conditions resulted in an increase of arable at the expense of pasture; elsewhere gain or loss of arable pasturage has been variable, but in England as a whole land under pasture is steadily increasing. This new pastureland can be made productive from the outset, owing to our increased knowledge of the uses of wild white clover (Gilchrist) and good pasture grasses (Stapleton at Aberystwyth), and the Rothamsted and other investigations. The modern demand for " young meat " is another incentive to grassland farming.

The adverse situation is also affected by a probably unavoidable specialization. Though keeping cattle and sheep, the east and north-eastern counties of England are still preponderantly arable, whereas in the north and north-west there is some arable mingled with the more general pasturage. Elsewhere in England the

[1] *Agricultural Atlas of England and Wales*, 1932.

cultivation and stock farming are more nearly equal. Where feeding stuffs are scarce in the arable east the farmers must pay heavy railway charges, while the dairy farmer of the west can buy more cheaply foreign products imported at Liverpool, Bristol and Plymouth. When feeding stuffs are plentiful in the region as a whole, home railway rates still add to the expense of the eastern farmer and prevent the western giving up his foreign in favour of the home supplies.

Agricultural Education was developing on sound lines throughout the nineteenth century. Soon after its initiation the Royal Agricultural Society of England began a series of experiments upon the growth of crops and fattening of livestock with special reference to manure and food. The Duke of Bedford of that time placed suitable land and buildings at the disposal of the Society for this purpose. The work of Sir John B. Lawes and Sir H. Gilbert at Rothamsted, near Harpenden in Hertfordshire, has already been touched upon, but it was not until considerably later that the working farmer, as distinguished from the agricultural expert, could receive any education in agriculture. In 1890, however, a tax levied on whisky was alienated to provide funds for the establishment of agricultural colleges and farm schools, of which, beginning with Bangor, eighteen such institutions were established during the next ten years. In 1909 Lloyd George devoted £2,000 out of public money for various Development Commissions which included a number of Agriculture Research Institutes. Among the Agricultural teaching and research institutions may be mentioned the University College of North Wales (Bangor), Colleges and Schools in South Wales, Kent, Yorkshire, at Cambridge, Reading, Penrith, Swanley, Uckfield, Chelmsford, Newcastle-on-Tyne (Armstrong

College) and the Eastern Counties Dairies' Institute at Ipswich. Many of these educational centres give degrees and certificates for agricultural proficiency and hold examinations for National Diplomas granted by the Royal and Highland Societies. A feature of several of these colleges is the farm, worked by the college staff. The free or low-priced leaflets issued by the Ministry of Agriculture and Fisheries give accounts of the latest scientific discoveries and practices in the pastoral world. The Rowett Institute at Aberdeen is one of the foremost centres in the British Isles for studying methods of cattle-rearing, and especially noteworthy is its work upon the diseases of hill sheep. The Welsh Plant Breeding Station established at Aberystwyth deals with the pastoral value of natural grasses and methods of improving natural pasture by the elimination of the poorer or harmful grasses and the introduction of nutritious growths. At Bangor work is being done on sheep matings in near degrees and upon sheep diseases and parasites, and in this connection special mention may be made of the Diseases of Animals Research Association in Scotland.

The first Dairy School was established by the British Farmers' Association and in due course was moved to Reading, where it is doing great work in connection with University College. The Farmers' Institutes at Cannington and elsewhere train special cheese makers. The Wool-Shearing Society gives advice to those desiring it on the treatment of wool and care in shearing.

Another outstanding development of the nineteenth and twentieth centuries has been the movement for combination and co-operation on the part of the farmers and distributors, in order to produce a standard commodity where guaranteed excellence and steady production should create a demand. Foremost among such co-operative efforts stands the combine known as The United Dairies Ltd., formed in 1915. It comprises a number of previously independent wholesale and retail milk districts ; the nucleus was a private company built up and operated by a group of Wiltshire farmers. It now possesses 70 creameries in milk-producing districts, and many factories for the production of cheese and preserved milk. All recent advance in the milk industry is due to its efforts and those of smaller independent companies composed mainly of farmers who hoped, by combination, to find a steady market for higher quality milk. It is largely owing to the U.D. that most of the London milk is pasteurized and tested for quality, as well as the advance in bottling. The U.D. controls 85 per cent of the London milk.

Other organizations for the protection and advancement of the Milk Distributors' interests are : The National Federation of Dairymen's Association, of which the U.D. is the most influential member ; the Amalgamated Master Dairymen, Ltd. ; the Northern Dairymen's Association, representing the interests of the smaller distributors. These first two Associations are centred in London, the last serves the north of England.

The chief retail organization is the Metropolitan Dairymen's Association for London, but in London the U.D. controls about 30 per cent of the retail milk trade.

Regarding milk producers, Co-operative Dairy Societies in England and Wales to the number of fifty or sixty trade in wholesale or retail markets, or else by a collective bargaining. The co-operation involved where creameries have been established has done much to standardize and regularize production. In Galloway numbers of creameries are placed near railways ; they are run by farmers who hold shares in them. One creamery is controlled by the Scottish Wholesale Co-operative Society, Glasgow; the Galloway Creamery Company is another. Motor lorries collect the milk, which is sent as liquid or as milk products to Newcastle, Birmingham, Liverpool, and even London.

Large-scale federation for the disposal of farm produce has not been attempted by the farming community as a whole, the British farmer generally preferring to make his own sale. He is rather suspicious of co-operation and federation. The organization known as the National Farmers' Union is very popular. It is concerned with such things as negotiation of contracts.

The Express Dairy is the best example of a successful, non-combine milk producing and distributing Company. It was established in 1864 and at the present moment has about 174 dairy branches in London. It possesses dairy farms at Finchley, Harrow Weald, Blackheath, Motting-ham, Mill Hill, Sudbury Park, Harefield, and Denham.

Another consequence of the increase and change in our sheep industry might find mention at this place. The introduction of the Blackface to the higher levels of the Scottish Highlands has brought into use land that was otherwise worthless, and must entail a steady appreciation of soil. In the Tweed Basin, however, there has been considerable natural deforestation through the ravages of sheep or rabbits upon young seedlings. The laying out of sheep walks here has also entailed deliberate deforestation, since the better forest land gives rise to the better grazing land. Much pine forest has gone and given place to heather and bracken, the young shoots of the former making good eating for sheep.

The replacement of the former wether flocks rising three to four years by a succession of young flocks sold off the hills in their first autumn is having a bad effect

s

upon hill pasture where the rough grass formerly consumed by the wethers in the autumn assisted the growth of nutritious herbage ready for the following spring. Apart from the manurial effects of the feeding wethers the removal of rough grass by nibbling gives opportunity for the growth of better herbage. Moreover, the younger sheep individually take more out of the soil for any given period than the older sheep of the other arrangement.

Still, much may be and is being done to help the hill pastures. The grass of upland peat moss is greatly improved by burning; and firing dry herbage each spring promotes new growths. Where old heather is burnt, new shoots spring up from seedlings or from the ancient stumps and make better grazing than the older plants. The re-heathering, however, is sometimes so slow that inferior herbage, such as blaeberry (bilberry) and blow-grass gain a permanent footing before the new heather has established itself. When heather land can be irrigated by water carried to it in sheep drains, a year or two suffices to turn it into grassland pasture.

## CHAPTER XXI

## HANDING ON THE HERITAGE

IN the foregoing chapters we have followed the pastoral heritage of Britain from its beginnings on the uplands, through the domestic and large-scale phases of the Middle Ages, the great progress in food and breeding of the eighteenth and nineteenth centuries and down to the collateral developments in science, education and co-operation.

At the present moment our industry is experiencing a decline which pessimists regard as permanent. The first import of corn sounded the knell of our grain cultivation,[1] and farmers sought salvation by farming for meat. Initial success along this line became imperilled by the overseas consignments of cattle and sheep, dead and alive, from countries where large-scale production and co-operation or expert distribution made for a reliable import of good meat, underselling possibly the second, and certainly the lower, grade home product. This or overseas competition was rendered more disastrous for British farmers by the invention of the refrigerator, which permitted British consumers to obtain the cheap imported product in excellent condition and taste.

The exigencies of war, enforcing the market, did much to remove the early prejudices against foreign meat, and the more skilful breeding and feeding which is now a

[1] But note the Wheat Act of 1934, whereby farmers producing grain at less than cost price are to be subsidized by the Government.

quality of overseas farming has increased the attraction of this supply.    To-day about one-half of the meat consumed in Britain is foreign, and the amount is steadily increasing.

"Empire" meat is not the only competition the home producer has to face.    Frozen beef once coming from Australia is less popular with the English market than Argentine chilled meat, which can hardly be distinguished from fresh beef, so that Australian beef now comes to us chiefly as "canned" meat.    New Zealand is our strongest competitor in the muttons, and the good qualities of Canterbury lamb have made it almost unrivalled in its sphere of sale.

The flowing tide of foreign competition is by no means confined to meat.    Our chief English cheeses are of sufficient individual and good quality to hold their own in the British market, but 90 per cent of the cheese we make is definitely second-class, and competes adversely with Australian and Canadian cheese.    The market for our best cheeses, as for our first-class beef or mutton, is with the wealthier consumers who can afford to pay more than the colonial price.

Our large imports of foreign butter can be traced to the Franco-German War, when Normandy butter, having lost its customary Paris market, was sent to England, a reduced export being continued after the Peace.    The taste for butter was growing among a population whose forebears ate their bread with dripping or lard, and Denmark, seeking commercial salvation in her newly established dairy industry, satisfied British needs with a low-priced standard butter of good quality.    Later our overseas dominions followed the example of Denmark, and to-day "Empire Butter" has become a household slogan.    There is also a considerable consignment from the Argentine.    English butter is still in demand, but its sale is generally local, and much of it is consumed on the producing farm.

Our import of fresh milk is negligible compared with home supplies, but there is a large import of condensed and powdered milk and cream.

The import of wool is many times the total of the home clip, a circumstance reflecting the healthiness of our textile industry. The Empire supplies the greater part of this import, though the Argentine Republic sends some, and of the remaining imports the fine Silesian merino is the most noteworthy on account of its felting property.

India, Italy, Germany, Argentine, Union of South Africa send us hides, and Australia, New Zealand, and the Union of South Africa sheepskins, a further reflection upon the extent of our manufacturing industries which have grown beyond the home resources of raw material. Unfortunately the British producer must ask the low price of the foreigner if he wish for a market, even though the expenses of production are greater here than abroad. This criticism applies to most of our home productions, overseas organization for co-operation, inspection, and sale, resulting in a marketable commodity of unfailing standard and regular supply. The purchaser knows that if he is not buying the best, at least he is getting good value for the money he disburses. The shipping of large quantities under one agent and from one port reduces transport costs, while large freightages, even over enormous distances, are proportionally very much less expensive than the small freightages dispatched by farmers individually disposing of their produce. Foreign countries, too, do much to help foreign exports to gain a footing over here, in spite of import duties. Low wages, accepted in some countries, greatly help foreign cheap production.

However, there are a few encouraging factors. The British *best* cannot be beaten, and whether of beef, mutton, or cheese, that best will always find good purchasers. Even our wool is of a character to make it in high demand in certain foreign factories and nearly one-half of the home clip is exported. It is noteworthy that Britain rears almost four-fifths the number of sheep produced in New Zealand and almost one-quarter the total reared in Australia, in spite of its special sheep industry.[1]

The British Isles hold and probably always will hold the proud position of the world's " stud farm ". It is true that apart from the indigenous breeds of our hills and marshes British breeds, in their improved forms, are products of the experimentation of the eighteenth and nineteenth centuries, but the experiments were undertaken on stock whose characteristics have been the work of slow adaptation to special environmental conditions, and the special aptitude of the stock raisers. Where conditions have been inclement the breeds have developed a constitutional hardiness which carries them through the bleak times and gives them power to thrive gloriously under better conditions.[2] Breeds of cattle evolved on the richer valley bottoms have acquired qualities that fit them for removal to similar environments elsewhere.[3] The sheep native to rough and bleak mountain or fell pasturage, where winter is spent in the open, develop a thick coat of long, flowing wool, wide feet to grip the rocks, and a nimbleness commensurate with the necessary daily range over the not very nutritious moorland.[4] The Oxford Down sheep are peculiarly

[1] 1933 statistics :—(in round numbers) Great Britain, 27,000,000 ; N.Z., 29,000,000 ; Australia, 112,000,000.

[2] E.g. Welsh Runts.

[3] Severn and Wye Valley Breeds.    [4] E.g. Herdwicks.

fitted to loamy soils and arable farming, and the ancestral discomforts of the Cotswold sheep produced a type still thriving best under hard conditions.   In fact the variety of the British sheep which enables us to supply so many dissimilar regions of the world is directly due to the great diversity of environments that go to make up Britain. Our Down sheep are not suited for rich pastures, our longwools are not profitable on the Downs, our lowland breeds do badly on hills or mountains, and for sheep rearing to be carried on with profit, different breeds may have to be kept in dissimilar districts even if of equal elevation on account of the differences in the herbage and water drainage arising from differences in the soil.   In some way or other all sheep are influenced by the soil of their habitat.[1]   This influence of climate and soil on the development and maintenance of our different breeds makes their classification difficult.   The geographical differentiation of lowland, Down, upland, and mountain has already been considered.   The sheep of the uplands and highlands generally are very active and of small or middle size with finely grained flesh of a venison flavour.   They are the sheep for pastures where the keep is rather scanty ; they *fatten* on unaccustomed good feeding.   When carefully bred they improve in bone and size, but lose in mutton flavour.   Low-country pastures and marshlands where the grass is rich and often rank, suit a large-boned fleshy animal, but their flesh is insipid, generally coarse-grained and less nutritious than that of the hill breeds ; there is often an undue proportion of fat.   When wool was sold for high prices such sheep were raised for their fleeces, but

[1] This and the preceding remarks are not intended to apply to sheep transferred from one region to another for fattening, the conditions being special.   " Flying flocks ", moved out of their right environment, do not leave progeny to deteriorate in succeeding generations.

to-day wool is a secondary matter, though sometimes important. Their meat makes one prefer the imported meat, but they are invaluable for crossing, the ram passing on his good qualities of large size and excellent wool, so that to obtain a good half bred one has only to select the ewe.

When the environment provides dry lair, light rainfall, mildish climate, the natural covering is a short wool. These conditions are found to some extent upon the well-drained Romney Marsh, but the winter is bleak and the native sheep are of the long-woolled variety. Apart from the chemical quality of the soil, dryness of climate affects the character of the herbage. Downland herbage is short, but different from that of the limestone soils farther north, where the rainfall is greater and the sheep of a different type.

The old Norfolk ewe, after centuries of poor heath keep, has become a slow feeder, long in the legs, and has acquired some of the heath breed qualities. On the wetter South Downs the sheep, still a heath breed, have longer and thicker fleeces and shorter legs than the old Norfolk breed—the legumes in the " chalk " grass give a richer feed and they have not to travel so far to eat their fill as in the case of the old Norfolks. The Southdown mutton is superior, a legacy from the early days of varied diet. The Scotch Blackface gives the good mutton of the heath breed it is by origin, but a result of its removal to its present habitat has lengthened its fleece as protection against the more severe climate.

Where the habitat includes a generally damp soil, the native breeds open their claws widely so as not to sink in, and the hard skin between the digits is not easily scraped off when in contact with long, wet herbage or when the sheep are penned on gritty arable land. When the soil is generally dry the feet open very slightly. Thus on the Downs, rarely sufficiently wet for the sheep to tread through the turf, the skin of the feet is softer, the claws close up together, and the feet are small compared with those of sheep on rich pastures. Downland sheep removed to an " open-toe " environment are liable to get the skin broken, and a consequent admission of the parasite of foot-rot.

The Lincoln sheep are much valued for their wool, particularly in demand at home and abroad for the manufacture of certain textiles. The peculiar lustre of the wool, however, is lost or greatly reduced when the sheep are reared in habitats dissimilar to their native habitat. The wool of sheep breeds developed in limestone areas is somewhat harsh, especially in contrast to those whose habitat is on clay or gravel soils. The wool of Leicester sheep bred north of the Tweed deteriorates both in quality and quantity. The more particularly geological aspect of the soil must be taken into account. The London clay of the London and Hampshire Basin is largely in grass. The clays of the central and southern parts of England (lias, Oxford, kimmeridge, Weald, and gault clays) provide low or undulating country also mostly given up to pasture. The Downs and Wolds constituting the upper chalk make the habitat of the Southdown sheep and other breeds. Arable agriculture combined with sheep folding occupies the farms of the free working soils of the great oolite and the light thin soils of the lower chalk. The red keuper marl of the triassic series constitutes the fertile and red marly soil of the English Midlands, whose rich pastures are under some marine influences coming in through the Midland, Severn and other " Gates ", influences which promote the high quality of the native Cheshire, Cheddar and other cheeses. The short, sweet herbage of the Pennine mountain limestones is eminently suitable for sheep, Blackface and other hill breeds on the higher, Leicester on the less elevated levels.  The thin soil of the bleak and rocky granite moorlands and the gneissic districts of north-west Scotland and the Hebrides, makes arable agriculture impossible, but there are good sheep and cattle walks.  The shales and slates of the Cambrian beds of Wales can only take sheep and cattle of the hill breeds, except where soil has collected in lower, sheltered river valleys.

This specialization of breed according to soil and climate becomes particularly evident when animals of the same parentage are removed to districts unlike those in which the type features were acquired, a noticeable change taking place within a few generations. The sheep gradually become lighter or darker in face, the wool more open and longer, or shorter and closer according as the new climate is wetter or drier than the old one.  The texture varies in coarseness, etc., the constitution and size of the animal changes, albeit slowly, and the accepted type is only maintained by a fresh importation of the original blood, making it necessary for the farm stock of the " new " worlds to be renewed from time to time from the home stock.

Without greatly reducing our imports there is still room for home expansion by means of certain improvements consisting mainly of improved methods of distribution and production.

On the distributing side there has lately been a considerable agitation for better marketing, and the Ministry of Agriculture has under consideration a plan for adapting the most promising of overseas methods to British conditions.  In England, perhaps only Scotch beef is *always* worthy of its high price, whereas the price correct for English meat of good quality one week may be demanded for inferior joints another, and this doubt as to the standard of purchase runs through many home-produced commodities. But we have already made a beginning with standard marks and national marks guaranteeing adequate inspection and quality, and advance may be expected along this line.

At the present time some quarter of a million cattle are delivered by the farmer at certain central abattoirs where they are killed, cut up, and the market found. The abattoir organization grades the meat and affixes the " mark " and the consumer buys the quality for which he pays. Butchers need not buy whole animals from the abattoir but only the joints they require. Sheep farmers are learning to combine into wool societies, which take over their wool, pack and sell it. These wool combines date from 1920 and exist in Kent and Yorkshire. The marketing of the country's milk would certainly lend itself to a mark for standard quality. The U.D. standard represents a good milk which satisfies consumers. A milk marketing board has already come into being.

The innate conservatism of the British farmer makes him suspicious alike of government and official interference, technical education, co-operative factories or collective distribution. He prefers to conform to tradition and will often continue to provide for a supply no longer in demand. Thus, in spite of the recently developed taste for " fancy " cheese, he continues his traditional manufacture, for which, it is true, he possesses the skill inherited from cheese-making forebears. With regard to meat, the modern trend is for small and tender joints, a trend which the decrease in the size of families is likely to perpetuate. Yet many farmers keep stock that hardly provides for these requirements. To-day " fat " joints are at a discount, the townsman, for example, generally preferring " lean " meat, but many farmers keep breeds of sheep whose meat is distinguished for its large proportion of fat.

Veal, baby beef, fattened lambs and tegs of good meat breeds need not come into foreign competition, and the farmer might rear for larger supplies of these commodities.  There could be more baby beef if more cows were born in the fattening districts, or young calves transported thither from urban or semi-urban areas where excellent cows are kept.  At present these young calves are sold for killing when only a few days old.  Calves purchased in the breeding districts for fattening as baby beef do not do so well, but this beef, killed at about one and a half years, requires about twice the quantity of concentrates for fattening as does three year old beef which would make the suggested increase unprofitable unless a cheaper source of concentrate could be found.

Distribution might be much improved by improving transport conditions.  At present foreign produce would appear to travel more cheaply on our railways than the home material.  In Wiltshire and Dorset the United Dairies Limited has organized an excellent system of road transport which links up the farm with the milk factory, and its enterprise might be imitated.  Some railways have already developed a good railway service for milk transport.  Trains composed of milk vans run on the L.N.E. Railway to Finsbury Park, on the L.M.S. Railway to Willesden, the G.W.R. to Paddington, and the S.R. to Clapham Junction ; there are specially reduced rates for the " long haul ".

The improvement to be expected from closer co-operation and better organization is denounced by many farmers as impossible in their industry.  The small farmer receives no better terms from a co-operative society or a combine acting as collector or middleman than does the large-scale producer, and he prefers to take the chance of a possible rise in the prices offered by a fluctuating market. Moreover, organization of husbandry by the State and by Limited Liability Companies has certain admitted disadvantages. It implies a species of time-table, whereas pastoral occupations are frequently dependent upon the variability of British weather and markets, necessitating daily modification of detail for which a headquarter supervision does not provide. Still, some co-operation for distribution has been satisfactorily effected, and to that already mentioned may be added such co-operative societies as the Harpenden Dairies Limited, instituted in January 1917, which sells the local milk retail in the village. The co-operation by farmers in Wiltshire and Somerset either to manufacture milk products or sell liquid milk is very small as compared with the quantity manufactured and sold by joint-stock enterprise. Most of the farm produce, however, especially from the small farmer, is sold without any visible guarantee of quality or any combined action for sale, and consequently when the produce is sold the farmers compete against each other and so depress their own prices without seriously affecting those of the overseas competitor. At the present time the great milk producing and consuming areas do not coincide, so that separate organizations have had to be established for wholesale and retail produce, and their interests are not always identical.

Co-operation in the marketing or distribution of farm produce should entail reduction in the number of middlemen operating between producer and consumer. An example of the present method is as follows : The fattened animal is sold for slaughter, the carcase, hide,

edible and inedible offal go to the district meat wholesaler, hide merchant, manure or bone meal manufacturer, soap boiler and dealer in edible offal. The
carcase may be sold to a second wholesaler for cutting
up for sale to the retail butcher, the edible offal going to
both the tripe-dresser and retail butcher. The hide
merchant sells to the tanner, and the tanner to the
leather goods manufacturer. Bones and waste meat
may return from the retail butcher to the wholesale offal
merchant, and thence to the manure and meal manufacturers, and so on. This system of middlemen is said
to add rather more than 100 per cent to the price paid
to the British farmer. Such a simple distribution may
have eight or nine middlemen, or market dues, or factory
personnel between the producer and final customer.
It has been suggested that half-way markets should be
deleted in the case of livestock, and replaced by a through
journey from the breeding to the finishing areas. On
the other hand, a case can be made out for the middleman, for British farmers are not, in general, good sales-
men, and without the middleman would have often
neither the knowledge, time, nor provision for personal
expenses to seek out and find the necessary market.
It has been argued that this employment of middlemen
at least finds work for them, an argument perhaps hardly
to be appreciated by impoverished farmers ; it has also
been held that labour efficiency might be increased by
greater use of machinery for milking, mixing, and carrying food to the animals. Actually, all well-equipped
farms do possess such machinery.

To-day sales are being encouraged by the use of
slogans of which " Eat More Fruit ", with possibly its
cream accompaniment, is the most agreeable. " Drink
More Milk " is becoming popular and may have some
effect as our consumption per head of liquid milk is

very low when compared with that of most other civilized countries.

Though ours is now essentially an industrial nation, the pastoral harvest of Britain could be increased if the land were utilized in a more scientific and reasonable way. In addition to the deterioration of hill pasture through the substitution of an annual succession of yearlings for matured wethers, there might be more supervision of the grassland. In mountain districts, especially in Wales, proper sub-division of the sheep walks would give opportunity for this better supervision, and allow, at need, for alternate periods of depasturing and recovery. Such " rotational " grazing might be extended to the lowlands. The even sward that makes for good grazing is only obtained by hard eating down and ripe herbage is of lower feeding value than before seeding. Mixed stock helps here, the sheep nibbling the sward closely and thus inducing a horizontal spreading of the plants rather than a high but smothering herbage. The best grasses make the best use of good conditions, but poorer conditions favour the poorer grasses. Under-grazing, by permitting the growth of thistles and rank weeds, has ruined much meadow pasture.

In many mountain districts the botanical composition results in some very poor pasture. The process of cutting down, grazing hard, and then manuring would promote great increase of better growths. It has been suggested [1] that much Welsh hill pasture could be improved by a preliminary burning of the herbage, scratching the surface with tractors, manuring with basic slag, nitrates, and chalk, and then scattering seed, especially white clover, on this prepared ground. The use of fences would ensure each sheep walk receiving a portion of this improved land, and if trees were planted

[1] Prof. White, Address, British Association, July 1932.

as shelter belts, sheep could be kept on the hills all the year round.    The poorer pastures of the fells or heather moorlands could be similarly improved.

In some cases forage crops suffer from too much water, which suitable draining would remove.    Such draining improves the herbage for hay and grazing and also removes deleterious parasites that might attack the livestock.    The Thames Valley Water Draining Scheme does not *prevent* the floods ; it removes water more quickly after they are over.

The unsuitability for grazing of much of our upland pasture, due to the species of the grasses, is increased by the fact that they receive no manuring other than that of the stock feeding upon them.    Phosphates are very beneficial for the growth of clovers and for keeping down weeds, and these and other artificial manures might help greatly.    It has been suggested that such manures could be carried by the air service to the "stormy hills of Wales."    Some upland pastures suffer from lack of water during the growing season so that grass cannot be grown for hay.    Lucerne, requiring less water than many growths, could be introduced with profit.

In general hill pastures are associated with sheep, but if a limited number of cattle were kept upon them they would obtain a more varied animal manure.    At the present time some former sheep pasture on the South Downs has been given up to cattle, and cattle have been proved very beneficial on the limestone pastures of the south coast where they tread down the grass.

There might also be some improvement in the quality of the feeding stuffs, leading to improvement in the animals themselves.    Improvement along these lines is going on with regard to dairy cattle.    The use of silos for stowing green grass or fodder in stacks or pits could be extended, especially when the hay harvest time is wet ; this would help the winter feeding of cows in milk when the other green food is unavailable.

Losses due to animal diseases are very serious ; bovine tuberculosis is expensive to cure and some animal diseases are dealt with drastically by a compulsory slaughter for which the State gives compensation. Between 1921 and 1933 foot and mouth disease cost the British Government £5,500,000 in compensation.

In spite of all the disturbing circumstances outlined above, our heritage from the past is a worthy one. We can still read in existing cathedrals, churches, cloth halls and roads, the gratitude of earlier generations, whether large-scale pastoral farmers or merchants of raw and manufactured pastoral products, while our link with Europe, forged in the excellence of our pastoral output and its derivatives, led the way to a general expansion of industry and trade that brought prestige as well as wealth to our Island kingdom.

Not less worthy is the heritage which has been or is being handed on overseas, a heritage both of men and their domestic stock. We have seen how the furtherance of sheep rearing in Scotland was accompanied by loss of farm and livelihood of very large numbers of the peasantry and small holders. The Highland crofts have supplied a constant stream of frugal and conscientious farm labourers to the developing agricultural lands of the Empire. The great evictions of the early years of the nineteenth century resulted in extensive settlements in Canada by English, Scotch and Irish farmers, and the work done by them and their descendants in opening up the Canadian backwoods and prairies is among the highest episodes of pioneer endeavour.

It is held that the sheep and cattle supplied to the world are practically the creation of the British farmer. They are, moreover, the best of their kind, and unequalled

T

by that of any other country. Always, during the nineteenth century, as the new land overseas became settled, recourse was had to British sheep and cattle. It is instructive to consider, if only in general terms, what breeds of such livestock we have despatched to other countries. Even recognizing the immensities of the countries to be stocked, the great varieties of British breeds have been equal to the task.

Beginning with our neighbour, Ireland, and then passing eastward to Europe generally, the tale is somewhat as follows : Ireland owes to Scotch blood the reclamation of her mongrel breed of cattle ; shorthorns and Galloways were early sent thither. To-day large numbers of Ayrshires are reared in Northern Ireland. The Leicester sheep both as a pure bred and for crossing is also much esteemed in Ireland. Austria possesses Red Polled Norfolk and Suffolk breeding stock, Belgium early acquired shorthorn bulls, Denmark Leicester sheep and Finland Ayrshire cattle.

After the Franco-German War, both France and Germany began to import our shorthorn bulls ; France also imports Devon cattle, Leicester sheep, and Hampshire Down lambs, Southdown lambs and shearlings. Germany, too, now imports the Red Polled Norfolk and Suffolk cattle for breeding stock, and Hampshire Down lambs. Leicester sheep go to Hungary ; Ayrshire cattle are found in Norway, shorthorns and Southdown lambs and shearlings in Russia. The early export of " Cotteswold " and other sheep in 1273, 1374 and in the later reigns of Edward IV and Henry IV " multiplied and increased greatly to the profit of Spain ". Ayrshires, Lincoln Red and shorthorn cattle are all to be found in Sweden.

Our breeds have gone in numbers to lands far overseas that lie outside the British Empire. In the United

States of America the annual import of sheep includes Oxford Downs, Dorset Horns, Leicesters, Border Leicesters, Rylands, Shropshires, Cheviots and Southdown rams, lambs, and shearlings. Among cattle the list includes the Hereford and shorthorn (earliest imports 1817 and 1837 respectively), Devon Red, Galloway, Polled Angus, Red Polled Norfolk and Suffolk, and Ayrshires. The Hereford is probably unrivalled as a ranch breed, being hardy and fattening on grass ; under desert or ranch conditions it can go without water for two or three days.

The two chief importing countries of British Stock in South America are the Argentine and Chile. The Argentine has a great import trade in Leicesters and Lincolns for crossing on the merino, the cross possessing an enhanced value in meat and wool. Romney Marsh sheep are bred in South Patagonia, whose harsh winter is no worse than that of their home country. Hampshire Down and Southdown lambs and shorthorn cattle are also imported. In South America generally are found the British shorthorn, Hereford, Lincoln Red and Aberdeen-Angus cattle ; the Suffolk sheep is also imported for improving the mutton of the merino. Chile takes Romney Marsh sheep and Southdown ram lambs and shearlings, whilst the latter are also sent to Japan.

It goes without saying that British breeds are widely disseminated throughout our Empire and its dependencies. Shorthorn Bulls and Red Polled Norfolk and Suffolk have made their entry into Egypt, while British South Africa rears the British shorthorn, Polled Angus, Ayrshire, Hereford, Lincoln Red and Devon breeds of cattle. The sheep of Canada include Oxford Down, Leicester, Border Leicester, Shropshire and Dorset Horn breeds, and among the cattle are the shorthorn (still most important), Polled Angus,

T*

Ayrshire, Devon, Lincoln Red, and Hereford, this last being introduced into Canada in 1861 and to Jamaica in 1845. The Falkland Isles give ideal pastures to Romney Marsh sheep.

A unique feature of the pastoral industry of New Zealand is the making of the Corriedale, a new breed developed since 1880. Prior to that time the New Zealand sheep, reared for their fleeces, were pure merino, but when it became possible to ship frozen carcases to London without deterioration to the meat, it was evident that the country would benefit greatly by rearing a better mutton sheep. With this end in view various English breeds were placed with the merino flocks, and after due experimentation it was found that the long-woolled mutton breeds, Lincoln, Cotswold and Leicester, were the best to cross on the merino ewe to obtain the desired type—producing at once good wool and good quality meat. The crosses were bred together and by culling from the flocks sheep showing undesirable qualities, and by limiting the breeding stock to its own flock, the required type was fixed. The Lincoln ram was the male parent more commonly used in developing the type. Its good quality wool and meat have made the Corriedale popular in New Zealand and Australia, to which countries it is almost entirely restricted. The wool is of medium staple, strong and light, while the mutton is superior to either of the parent breeds. The lamb carcase is the famous Canterbury lamb. It is not surprising that there are large annual exports of Lincoln and Leicester sheep to New Zealand, and the Shropshire and Romney Marsh have also found a home there. The cattle of New Zealand include the Ayrshire, short-horn, Aberdeen-Angus, and Hereford, the last three breeds being the favourite. Regarding Australia, a favourite sheep is the Shropshire, which is perhaps the most widely distributed of all the short-woolled breeds. There, as well as in New Zealand and North America, the Shropshire is much used for crossing.    The Leicester has played its part in the improvement of the fleeces in Australia, and this sheep, with Southdown ram lambs and shearlings, is still part of the annual importation. Romney Marsh sheep, Ayrshire, shorthorn, Polled Angus, Devon, and Hereford cattle are also found in Australia.

The above list may be regarded as a résumé of our whole theme.    It shows how diversified is our pastoral heritage, strengthened to meet adequately many conditions, and enabling us, without despoiling ourselves, to hand on the legacy we have received, not only to the future, but to the great spaces of the world.

# BIBLIOGRAPHY

AGRICULTURAL ATLAS OF ENGLAND AND WALES. REVISED
  EDITION, 1932. Prepared by MALCOLM MESSER.

BIRCH, R. W. P. . . *The Disposal of Town Sewage*, 1870.
  *Sewage Irrigation by Farmers*, 1878.

BLUNDELL, F. N. . . *A New Policy for Agriculture*, 1931.

BRIDGES, A., and JONES, *The Midland Grazing Industry*, 1931.
  A. G.

BRUCE, A. B., and *Crop and Stock Improvement*, 1926.
  HUNTER, H.

CAMBRIDGE UNIVERSITY *Great Britain, Essays in Regional*
  PRESS. EDITOR A. G. *Geography*, 1928.
  OGILVIE

CARRIER, E. H. . . *Water and Grass : A Study in the
  Pastoral Economy of Southern
  Europe*, 1932.

COFFEY, W. C. . . . *Productive Sheep Husbandry* (Revised, 2nd ed.), 1929.

COLEMAN, JOHN . . *The Cattle, Sheep and Pigs of Great
  Britain*, 1887.

DARBY, H. C. . . . " Human Geography of the Fenland
  before the Drainage ", *Geographical
  Journal*, November 1932.

DIXON, H. N. . . . *Field and Fern : or Scottish Flocks
  and Herds* (North and South,
  2 vols.), 1865.

GRANT, I. F. . . . *Everyday Life on an old Highland
  Farm*, 1924. *Social and Economic
  Development of Scotland before
  1603*, 1930.

GREGORY, J. W. . . *The Story of the Road from the beginning down to* A.D. *1931*.

KING, F. H. . . . *Irrigation and Drainage* (7th ed.),
  1911.

LONG, JAMES . . . *Modern Sheep Farming*, 1917.

MALDEN, W. J. . . . *British Sheep and Shepherding*, 1915.
  *Actual Farming : Its Processes and
  Practices*, 1925. *Grassland Farm-
  ing : Pastures and Leys*, 1924.

281

McCombie, William . *Cattle and Cattle Breeders* (2nd ed.), 1875.

Orr, John . . . . *A Short History of British Agriculture, 1922. Grass and Hay Farming: An Economic Study, 1931.*

Orwin, C. S. . . . *The Future of Farming, 1930.*

Peake, H. . . . . *The English Village: The Origin and Decay of its Community, 1922.*

Pratt, E. A. . . . *A History of Inland Transport and Communications in England, 1912.*

Prewett, F. J. . . *The Marketing of Farm Produce, I. Livestock, 1926. The Marketing of Farm Produce, II. Milk, 1927.*

Prothero, R. E. . . *The Pioneers and Progress of English* (Baron Ernle) *Farming, 1888. English Farming, Past and Present (4th ed.), 1927. The Land and its People; Chapters in Rural Life and History, 1925.*

Rowe, R. R. . . . *Report upon the Sewage Works of some Towns in England, 1869.*

Russell, Sir E. John *Manuring for Higher Crop Production (2nd ed.), 1917. The Farm and the Nation, 1933.*

Scott, John . . . *Irrigation and Water Supply, 1883.*

Scott, J., and Morton, *The Soil of the Farm, 1882.*
J. C.

Seebohm, M. E. . . *The Evolution of the English Farm,* (M. E. Christie) *1927.*

Shaw, T. J. . . . *The Summer Feeding of Livestock, 1930.*

Stamp, L. D., and *The British Isles: A Geographic and* Beaver, S. H. . . *Economic Survey, 1933.*

*Statesman's Year Book,* 1935.

Tatham, William . . *National Irrigation, or the Various Methods of Watering Meadows, 1801.*

White, R. . . . . *Sheep Farming: A Distinctive Feature of British Agriculture. Address: Brit. Ass., York, 1932.*

Wilson, James . . . *The Breeding and Feeding of Farm Stock, 1921. The Principles of Stock Feeding, 1927.*

Wood, T. B., and *Beef Production in Great Britain,* Newman, L. F. *1928.*

YOUATT, WILLIAM . . *The Sheep : their Breeds, Management, and Diseases, etc.,* 1837. *The Complete Grazier* . . . Enlarged, Revised and brought up to date by W. FREAM (15th ed.), edited by W. E. BEAR, 1908.

YOUNG, ARTHUR . . *Travels, etc. General View of the Agriculture of* [*various counties*], 1797–1804.

# I. INDEX OF GEOGRAPHICAL NAMES

Keswick, 217
Ketton, 98
Kidbrooke, 230
Killerby, 99
Kilmarnock, 193, 194
Kincardineshire, 100
Kingsteignton, 231
Kington, 148
Kirkcudbright, 167
Kirk Levington, 99
Knighton, 148
Kyle, 101

LAKE DISTRICT, 16–17, 64, 145, 200, 217, 249
Lammermuir, 245
Lanark (-shire), 122, 146
Lancashire, 16, 80, 146, 172–3, 195, 197, 216, 232, 243, 255
Land's End, 102
Leicester (-shire), 92, 95, 194, 199, 209, 211, 255
Leith, 127
Lerwick, 178
Lewes, 96, 169, 217
Lewis, 63, 65, 166
Lincoln (-shire), 29, 106, 122, 152, 165, 167, 194, 198, 218, 228
Liverpool, 115, 153, 180, 256, 259
Lleyn Peninsula, 22
Lockerbie, 168, 216
London (and suburbs), 42, 87, 101, 105, 155, 160, 165, 167, 169, 171, 176–7, 189, 192, 194–5, 200, 208–11, 215, 219–20, 230, 232, 244, 253, 258–9, 267, 270, 278
Long Mynd, 157
Lostwithiel, 201
Loughborough, 92, 94
Low Countries, 80, 84, 91, 215

MAN, Is. of, Manx, 143–4, 172, 226, 230, 233, 244
Mardale, 19, 249
Marlborough, 217
Maybole, 104
Mediterranean, 55
Melrose, 204
Melton, 199
Melton Mowbray, 199
Menai Sts., 64, 176
Mendip Forest, 63
Merioneth, 148
Midlands (English), 13, 37–9, 54, 93, 96, 142, 149, 152, 173, 175–6, 178, 180, 187, 190, 193, 195, 209–10, 243, 267
Monmouth, 177
Montgomeryshire, 147–8, 171
Moray Firth, 180, 205
Morfe Common, 157
Mottingham, 259
Musselburgh, 127

NAIRN, 166

Nen Basin, 193
Netherlands, 189
Newcastle-on-Tyne, 218, 230, 256, 259
New Zealand, 262–4, 278–9
Nidderdale, 227
Norfolk, 10, 62, 85–7, 91, 106, 139, 167–8, 173, 186, 211
Normandy, 177, 262
Northallerton, 99
Northampton (-shire), 106, 158, 161, 167, 193, 209, 211, 233–4, 255
Northumberland, 95, 112, 154, 160, 180, 245
Norway (Norse), 63, 91, 145, 276
Norwich, 129, 193, 211
Nurstead, 230

ORKNEY Is., 144–6, 172, 178
Osbournby, 122
Oswestry, 197
Ouse, R., 105, 108, 112
Overton, 217
Oxford (-shire), 158, 194, 198, 200, 217, 231, 253

PALESTINE, 236
Paris, 133, 262
Parret, R., 110
Patagonia, 277
Peak District, 147
Peebles (-shire), 124, 192
Pembroke (-shire), 176, 195
Pennines, 65, 249, 267
Penrith, 99, 160, 256
Perth (-shire), 122, 166
Peru, 137
Pevensey, 41, 110–11, 169
Plymouth, 128, 256
Plympton St. Mary, 128
Portmadoc, 64
Portobello, 127
Potteries, The, 197
Potton, 250
Preston, 218–19, 226
Provence, 59, 63–4
Purbeck, 150
Pyecombe, 248

RADNOR, 64, 148, 171
Rawcliffe, 112
Reading, 256–7
Rhône, R., 60
Romford, 129
Romney Marsh, 32–5, 110–11, 210, 249, 266
Ross, 166, 207
Rothamsted, 138, 255–6
Russia, 276

SAFFRON WALDEN, 251
Salisbury, 217, 246
Saltersbrook, 250
Savoie, 60
Scalford, 199

# II. SUBJECT INDEX